Tributes to Paul Dirac

Portrait of Professor P A M Dirac, OM, FRS in oils, painted by Michael Noakes in 1978 and now hanging in the Hall of St John's College, Cambridge. (Courtesy the Master and Fellow of St John's College, Cambridge.)

Tributes to Paul Dirac

edited by

J G Taylor

*King's College,
University of London*

Adam Hilger, Bristol

British Library Cataloguing in Publication Data

Tributes to Paul Dirac.
   1. Dirac, P. A. M.
   I. Taylor, John, *1931–*   II. Dirac, P. A. M.
   530.1'092'4   QC16.D5

   ISBN 0-85274-480-3

Consultant Editor: **Professor R H Dalitz,** University of Oxford

Published under the Adam Hilger imprint by IOP Publishing Ltd
Techno House, Redcliffe Way, Bristol BS1 6NX, England

Printed in Great Britain by J W Arrowsmith Ltd, Bristol

Contents

Part II: Dirac's Contributions to Physics and Mathematics

List of Contributors

R H Dalitz, Department of Theoretical Physics, University of Oxford, 1 Keble Road, Oxford OX1 3NP, UK

C J Eliezer, Department of Mathematics, La Trobe University, Bundoora, Victoria, Australia

P Goddard, Department of Applied Mathematics and Theoretical Physics, University of Cambridge, Silver Street, Cambridge CB3 9EW, UK

Lady B Jeffreys, 160 Huntingdon Road, Cambridge CB3 0LB, UK

J E Lannutti, Physics Department, Florida State University, Tallahassee, Florida 32306, USA

Sir James Lighthill, University College London, Gower Street, London WC1, UK

P T Matthews, Department of Applied Mathematics and Theoretical Physics, Cambridge University, Silver Street, Cambridge CB3 9EW, UK

J Mehra, 7830 Candle Lane, Houston, Texas 77071, USA

Sir Rudolf Peierls, Department of Nuclear Physics, University of Oxford, Keble Road, Oxford OX1 3RH, UK

R J N Phillips, Rutherford Appleton Laboratories, Chilton, Oxon OX11 0QX, UK

J C Polkinghorne, The Vicarage, 24 Tyler Hill Road, Blean, Canterbury CT2 9HT, UK

Abdus Salam, Department of Theoretical Physics, Imperial College, Prince Consort Road, London SW7 2BZ, UK
also at: International Centre for Theoretical Physics, 34100 Trieste, PO Box 566 – Miramare, Strada Costiera 11, Italy

S Shanmugadhasan, Herzberg Institute of Astrophysics, National Research Council of Canada, Ottawa, Ontario, Canada K1A 0R6

J G Taylor, King's College London, Department of Mathematics, Strand, London WC2R 2LS, UK

E Wigner, Department of Physics, Princeton University, Princeton, NJ 08544, USA

Preface

This book is a tribute to one man, Paul Dirac. He was a very great theoretical physicist and a great man. We are all honoured to have had him amongst us. The following pages are a tribute to his qualities, both from the general and technical viewpoints. I would like to thank the contributors for their help in bringing this tribute to a wider audience. I would also like to thank Jim Revill of Adam Hilger and Professor Richard Dalitz of the University of Oxford for their unstinting work behind the publishing scenes, as well as Dr Alan Macfarlane and the Master and Fellows of St John's College, Cambridge for their help in holding the Memorial Conference and Dinner in the first place.

J G Taylor
King's College, London, August 1986

Introduction

P T Matthews

This volume is based on the papers presented at the Memorial Meeting for Paul Adrien Maurice Dirac which was held in Cambridge on 19 April 1985 and on the speeches made at the dinner in St John's College on the same evening, together with a biographical sketch and reminisences of Dirac by some of his many colleagues and students. The meeting was organised by Professor J G Taylor as part of the programme of the Mathematical Physics Group of The Institute of Physics and was deliberately timed to combine with the Memorial Service for Dirac which was held in St John's College Chapel on the following day.

Dirac's unassuming, but awe-inspiring, spirit could be felt almost tangibly throughout the proceedings because the surroundings were so closely associated with him. He had entered St John's College as an unknown research student in 1923, established an international reputation within two years and remained a member of the College until his death. He was Lucasian Professor of Mathematics (Newton's Chair) in the University of Cambridge for nearly 40 years. The Memorial Meeting itself was held in the Arts School where Dirac delivered his lectures based on his famous book and nearly all the speakers and many in the audience had had the privilege of learning quantum mechanics from Dirac personally under that same roof.

The Meeting itself was an opportunity for a number of Dirac's pupils and their successors to express their admiration for one of the chief architects of quantum mechanics and one of the greatest theoretical physicists of all time. In 1925 Heisenberg proposed the use of non-commuting matrices in the quantum description of atomic phenomena. Within a few months Dirac had developed this

1

rather tentative proposal into his powerful relation between Poisson brackets and quantum commutators and removed, at a stroke, the apparent incompatibility between classical and quantum physics, which had been baffling physicists for 25 years. Before he had time to capitalise on this breakthrough, Schrödinger produced his wave equation and established the relation between this and Heisenberg's matrices. Again, in a matter of months, with his powerful and pragmatic use of the δ-function, Dirac produced the complete 'transformation theory' formulation of quantum mechanics, a generalisation of the above ideas, which has never been improved upon apart from Dirac's own brilliant invention of the bra–ket notation which came some years later. The development of transformation theory was followed immediately by Dirac's quantisation of the radiation field, showing how the Planck–Einstein conjecture of photons emerged naturally from the new theory and the relativistic quantum theory of the electron, leading to the completely unanticipated prediction of the positron. It is true that the 'tide in the affairs of men' came at exactly the right time for Dirac, but the courage and panache with which he rode in on it produced a display of creative genius which bears comparison with other great intellectual achievements in any field. In the articles collected here the story of these early developments is given by Professor Mehra. Professors Lighthill and Polkinghorne deal, respectively, with the mathematical developments which have subsequently legitimised Dirac's δ-function and with some of the philosophical questions relating to the physical interpretation of quantum mechanics. The articles by Professor Salam, Dr Goddard and Professor J G Taylor all deal with more topical subjects, but so pervasive was Dirac's influence that these too have their roots in his later work.

Dirac was not only a great physicist; he was also a great man. His modesty and his reticence are legendary. Whenever he did express a view on any subject it was done with the utmost clarity and honesty. All who were lucky enough to get to know him speak of his kindness. His generosity, particularly in his assessment of the work of his colleagues and contemporaries was outstanding. As a mark of respect and affection this volume is dedicated to his memory.

A Biographical Sketch of the Life of Professor P A M Dirac, OM, FRS

R H Dalitz

1902

Paul Adrien Maurice Dirac was born at 15 Monk Road, Bishopston, a suburb of Bristol, on 8 August. His parents were Charles Adrien Ladislas Dirac and Florence Hannah (née Holten) who had married at the Portland Street Methodist chapel in Kingsdown, a suburb of Bristol, on 22 July 1899. His father Charles had been born in 1866 at Monthey, a large town in the French-speaking part of the canton of Valais in Switzerland, had attended lectures at the University of Geneva for the year 1887–8 and had come to Bristol as a French tutor at some time before 1896. Dirac's mother had been born in 1878 at Liskeard in Cornwall but her family had moved to Bristol in about 1880 when her father took up a post as master mariner on a Bristol ship. In September 1896, Charles Dirac took up a position as French lecturer at the Merchant Venturers Technical College, Bristol, a substantial trade school with sections at the preparatory, secondary and tertiary levels. In 1909, the engineering sections of the tertiary training were made part of the newly chartered University of Bristol. In 1919, the secondary school split off, moving to a new site on Cotham Hill and taking the name 'Cotham Secondary School for Boys', and Charles Dirac went with it, remaining with the school (known today as Cotham Grammar School) as French teacher until his retirement in 1931.

Paul had two siblings, an older brother named Reginald Charles Felix born on 15 April 1900 and a younger sister named Beatrice Isabelle Marguerite Walla born on 4 September 1906. Each of Charles Dirac's children was registered at birth as a Swiss citizen of the commune of St Maurice in the canton of Valais.

1907–18

Paul's primary education was at the local school, the Bishop Road Elementary School. His early upbringing appears to have been rather severe, for his father was known to be a strict disciplinarian, certainly so in the school and apparently even more so at home. The children were required to speak only grammatically exact French at the dinner table and Paul always attributed his taciturnity to this circumstance; as a child at home he often did not speak because he did not find it easy to say what he wished in French, as was required of him. His mathematical abilities had already become apparent at primary school. He entered the secondary school of the Merchant Venturers Technical College, where his father taught, at age 12 years, somewhat younger than was usual. The education provided was strong in the academic subjects, but had a practical orientation. Modern languages were taught for use, and there was some history and geography, but no classics or literature; the secondary school was particularly good for mathematics and sciences, because the laboratory facilities of the Technical College were available to it and because it had good teachers, some of whom also taught at higher levels in the Technical College. Paul was soon far out in front of the other students in mathematics and was given more advanced books to study and projects to carry out, separate from his class.

1918–23

Paul matriculated in 1918 to become a student of electrical engineering at the University of Bristol. Since the Engineering Department of the university was part of the Technical College, he continued his studies in the same building as he had previously done his schoolwork. He regularly did first-class work throughout his course and gained first-class honours in his final examinations for the BSc degree in electrical engineering in 1921. He competed late in the 1920–1 academic year for a scholarship to enter St John's College, Cambridge, and was awarded an Open Exhibition which he was not able to take up since his family did not have the means to support him as a student at Cambridge. He sought a job as an electrical engineer but did not find one. The Mathematics Department at the University of Bristol then proposed that he might take their course of lectures in two years as an unofficial student, paying no tuition fees, an offer which he accepted. In the final mathematics examination in 1923 he was the top student, with first-class honours. He was awarded a research studentship by the Department of Scientific and Industrial Research and was accepted by St John's College, Cambridge, as a postgraduate student in mathematics, receiving from them also the Exhibition he had won in 1921.

On 18 August 1919, Charles Dirac gave up the Swiss citizenship of himself and his children, thus releasing them all from their rights and obligations in the commune of St Maurice. Charles Dirac became British by naturalisation on 22 October 1919.

1923–6

On arrival at Cambridge, Paul Dirac was allotted Dr R H Fowler as research supervisor. His early work was on problems involving effects of relativity on statistical mechanics, where the quantum theory was peripheral, but he soon moved on to developing some

The youthful Paul Dirac, circa 1925. Printed in the 1937 issue of the school magazine, the Old Cothamian.

aspects of the use of Niels Bohr's old quantum theory. Then, at the end of July 1925, Heisenberg visited Fowler at Cambridge, spoke at the Kapitza Club, and told Fowler privately a little about his new work on the quantum theory of electrons in atoms. After his return to Göttingen, Heisenberg sent Fowler a proof copy of his paper about this work, and Fowler passed it on to Dirac for study late in August. Heisenberg's paper was not really finished work. Following a particular line of thought, Heisenberg had been led to consider quantities which depended on two atomic states and then to propose a definite multiplication rule for them which was later recognised to be that of matrix multiplication. In particular, Heisenberg drew attention to the fact that the result of his multiplication rule depended on the order in which the multiplication was carried out, quite a novel situation. But what could its meaning be?

At first sight, Dirac could see no sense in Heisenberg's result and he put the paper aside for a few weeks. When he looked at it again, he realised that the failure of this multiplication to commute was really the essential point of this paper and he focused attention on the amount by which the multiplication of two quantities A and B failed to commute, the quantity $(AB - BA)$, called the commutator. After some thought, it came to him suddenly that this commutator might correspond to a quantity he had seen occur in the theory of classical dynamics and he soon established that these commutators had a natural interpretation as the Poisson brackets of classical dynamics. This led him quickly to his first major paper,[1] a paper which was published early in 1926 and established him at once as a highly original worker in this field at the international level. His idea was that the variables in classical dynamics, position x and momentum p, became 'q-numbers' in quantum theory, and that these q-numbers did not necessarily commute with each other, their commutator being given by the classical Poisson bracket, when the variables were replaced by the appropriate q-numbers. He was then able to calculate the properties of particular theories by algebraic methods, for example for the motion of an electron in a Coulomb field. In doing so[2] he showed that this system, a good model for the hydrogen atom according to Rutherford and Bohr, had quantised (discrete) energy levels which agreed with those of the Bohr atom.

This remarkable achievement led Dirac on to make rapid

progress in a number of directions, especially on the use of q-numbers[3] and on the treatment of systems with more than one electron,[4] and important papers came forth from Dirac in a stream over the next two years. In the spring of 1926 he wrote a very substantial PhD thesis of about 140 pages, entitled 'Quantum Mechanics', which developed these ideas and their applications, including an attempt (which he considered to be unsatisfactory) to extend them to cover the case of relativistic dynamics. In the Easter term of that year, he gave his first lecture course at Cambridge University, on the new subject of quantum mechanics, based for the most part on his own researches.

In 1925 he had been awarded a Senior Studentship of the 1851 Exhibition, which permitted him to study abroad. In September 1926 he went to Niels Bohr's Institute for Theoretical Physics at Copenhagen, where he benefited especially from long discussions with Bohr, a deep thinker who broadened Dirac's view of quantum theory. At Copenhagen Dirac prepared his major paper[5] on what has become known as transformation theory, which showed that Schrödinger's wave mechanics and his q-number quantum mechanics (or Heisenberg's matrix mechanics) were special cases of a more general formalism. In this paper, he showed that the description of a physical system can be based on any complete set of commuting variables, and that this led to an amplitude whose modulus squared gives the probability that an observation of these variables will give particular values for them. Wave mechanics is based on particle coordinates, whereas matrix mechanics uses the energy and any other constants of the motion as its commuting variables. In particular he showed that the transformation function defined by suitably specified conditions satisfies Schrödinger's equation, i.e. Dirac derived Schrödinger's theory from his q-number quantum mechanics. Of course, Schrödinger had already shown how to obtain Heisenberg's matrix from the wavefunction in his wave mechanics.

1927

At the beginning of February, Dirac moved to the University of Göttingen, where he interacted most of all with his fellow student J R Oppenheimer but had much discussion also with M Born, J Franck and I Tamm, the latter being a visitor from Russia of whom Dirac saw a great deal in later years. From Göttingen, he published two papers[6,7] on the interaction of electromagnetic radiation with atoms, introducing the notions of particle creation and annihilation in a precise way for the first time and developing the technique of 'second quantisation' in which the electromagnetic potentials become operators in the abstract space spanned by particle number. For example, using these methods he was able to derive from first principles the correct expressions for the *A*- and *B*-coefficients introduced by Einstein in his discussion of the statistical theory of the interaction between matter and radiation in equilibrium. These important papers really established the subject of quantum electrodynamics, our most successful theory in the domain of particle physics today and the model on which all other quantum field theories have been patterned. In a letter dated 19 February 1927 to Niels Bohr from Göttingen, Dirac also gave the first derivation of Lorentzian lineshape for photons emitted in a simple atomic transition. In April he moved on to Leiden, where he remained until late June, before returning to Cambridge.

In 1927 Dirac was elected a Fellow of St John's College, Cambridge, with which he was associated for the rest of his life. He then lived in college (New Court A staircase, room 4) and did most of his work there. At the end of October, he attended the Solvay Conference at Brussels for the first time and contributed significantly to the discussions. By the end of the year, he was tussling again with the problem of incorporating relativity into the quantum mechanics of the electron in a satisfactory way. He required that the equation to describe an electron should be first-order in both time and space derivatives and that its wavefunction $\psi(x)$ should lead to a positive definite probability density.

1928

Dirac found his famous four-component wave equation for the electron at the very end of 1927. In his notation, this reads[8,9]

$$\left(\frac{W}{c} - \boldsymbol{\alpha} \cdot \boldsymbol{p} - \beta mc\right)\psi = 0 \qquad (1)$$

where m, W are the electron's mass and total energy respectively, $\boldsymbol{p} = -i\hbar\nabla$ is the momentum operator, $\boldsymbol{\alpha}$ and β are four 4×4 matrices which satisfy $\alpha_i^2 = \beta^2 = 1$, $\alpha_i\alpha_j + \alpha_j\alpha_i = 2\delta_{ij}$ and $\alpha_i\beta + \beta\alpha_i = 0$ for i, $j = 1$ to 3, and $\delta_{ij} = 1$ if $i = j$, but is otherwise zero. $\hbar$, c denote $h/2\pi$, where h is Planck's constant, and the velocity of light, respectively. This equation satisfies the requirements just mentioned, the probability density being $\psi^{\dagger}(x)\psi(x)$, where $\psi^{\dagger}$ denotes the Hermitian conjugate of ψ and the wavefunction $\psi(x)$ is a 1×4 column matrix. As Dirac noted, its Lorentz-invariant character can be made more apparent by adopting a relativistic notation, equation (1) then leading to the form

$$\left(\sum_{\lambda=1}^{4} (\gamma_\lambda p_\lambda) - imc \right) \psi = 0 \qquad (2)$$

where $\gamma_4 = \beta$, $\boldsymbol{\gamma} = -i\beta\boldsymbol{\alpha}$ and $p_4 = iW/c$. When there is an electromagnetic field present, with scalar potential V and vector potential A, these equations are to be modified by the replacement of W by $(W + eV)$, and of p by $(p + eA/c)$, where e is the charge (negative) of the electron. For the form (1), this leads us to the equation

$$\left[\frac{W + eV}{c} - \boldsymbol{\alpha} \cdot \left(\boldsymbol{p} + \frac{e}{c}A \right) - \beta mc \right] \psi = 0. \qquad (3)$$

Equation (3) is certainly Dirac's most outstanding achievement in fundamental physics. Its implications were immense. It was immediately realised that it required the electron to have spin $\hbar/2$, as was observed and had appeared so mysterious, and the electron spin therefore became seen to be a consequence of special relativity. In the limit of small velocities, equation (3) was shown to reduce to the Schrödinger equation supplemented by the terms

$$\frac{e\hbar}{2mc} \boldsymbol{\sigma} \cdot H + \frac{ie\hbar}{2mc} \boldsymbol{\alpha} \cdot E \qquad (4)$$

the first of which states that the electron magnetic moment is $\mu = e\hbar/mc$, as is observed. W Gordon and C G Darwin independently solved Dirac's equation for an electron in a Coulomb field, obtaining the same formula as did Sommerfeld earlier on the basis of the old quantum theory, a result in excellent agreement with the experimental data available at that time and for the next 20 years. In particular, it reproduced the fine-structure splitting observed between the $^2P_{3/2}$ and $^2P_{1/2}$ states of hydrogen, while leaving the $n = 2\,^2S_{1/2}$ state degenerate with the latter, a degeneracy not resolved empirically until the Lamb–Retherford measurement of their separation ('the Lamb shift') in 1947.

On the other hand, Dirac pointed out in a lecture at Leipzig

University in June 1928 that his equation (3) also had solutions corresponding to the charge $(-e)$, or alternatively to negative energy states for the electron (charge $+e$), and that he did not yet have a satisfactory interpretation for them.

In August 1928, Dirac took up an invitation from the Russian Association of Physicists to speak at their Sixth Conference, held on a boat on the River Volga. He found this a most enjoyable and successful visit and he subsequently visited the USSR every year, excepting 1931, up to his last pre-war visit in 1937.

1929

At the beginning of this year, Dirac was engaged in writing his magnum opus, *The Principles of Quantum Mechanics.* However, during the months of May and June, he lectured at the University of Wisconsin at Madison, and in July at the University of Michigan Summer School at Ann Arbor. He then joined Heisenberg, who had been lecturing at the University of Chicago, and they travelled together across the Pacific Ocean to visit Japan. They both gave lectures at Tokyo and Kyoto, which were long remembered there. They then parted company, Dirac making his way to Vladivostock, to take the trans-Siberian railway to Moscow, where he met Tamm and other Russian friends before continuing on his way back to Cambridge, Heisenberg returning to Leipzig by way of Hong Kong and India.

In 1929 Dirac was appointed to a University Lectureship in Mathematics at Cambridge, beginning in October. In order to make sure that Dirac need take on no teaching more than the minimum required by his University Lectureship, St John's College acted quickly to establish a special college post for him, a Praelectorship in Mathematical Physics.

The problem of the negative energy states, mentioned above, remained on Dirac's mind. He realised that it would be possible to define the 'vacuum' as the configuration in which each negative energy state was occupied by an electron. If one negative-energy state were unfilled the 'hole' would behave like a positive-energy particle of charge $(-e)$; he already knew mathematical ways to demonstrate this for electrons not interacting with each other, but the question of the interaction between this positively charged 'particle' and the electrons filling the other negative-energy states left him uneasy. The only positively charged particle then known was the proton; could this 'hole' perhaps be attributed to the proton? This question was much debated through this period, and many senior physicists favoured the proton interpretation. Dirac himself felt that this positive particle should have the same mass as the electron, but went along with the majority opinion for its interpretation as a proton for some time, as his papers [11,12] indicate, although the second of these papers does demonstrate that the proton and electron in a hydrogen atom should then annihilate rather quickly, contrary to observation. This unsatisfactory situation persisted for some considerable time, for it was not until 1931 that Dirac predicted firmly (in a paper [13] primarily on another topic, see below) that there should exist a positively charged 'anti-electron' with the same mass as the electron. These uncertainties were resolved only when the anti-electron, now known as the positron, was discovered by Anderson in August 1932 and quickly confirmed at Cambridge by the work of Blackett and Occhialini, who were the first to publish (in February 1933) pictures of positron tracks.

1930

Dirac's book appeared in its first edition, which sold out quite quickly. It was recognised, and still is, as the major work on quantum mechanics, the definitive work which all physicists sought to understand.

He was elected to the Royal Society in March, upon the first suspension of his certificate of candidature, an unusual occurrence. His citation needed to consist of little more than a list of the papers 1 to 10 on our select list, given below, which were published before 1930. Their pioneering importance made the case for his election self-evident.

1931

Dirac moved on to totally new ground in a paper [13] investigating the consequences of the existence of a magnetic monopole. He raised new topological questions concerning classical electromagnetic fields, demonstrating that acceptable quantum mechanics was possible for an electron moving in the field of a magnetic monopole only if its pole strength g satisfied the condition $ge = n\hbar c/2$ for some integer n. This apparent quantisation condition for electric charge aroused great interest, in view of its novelty and its suggestive character.

In this year he was elected a Corresponding Member of the Academy of Sciences of the USSR.

In the summer, he visited the USA, making a long walking trip on the trails of Glacier National Park, with J H van Vleck and others. He then settled at Princeton University as Visiting Professor for the Fall term and gave a series of lectures on quantum mechanics.

1932–3

Dirac now wrote the first [14] of three important papers on relativistic field theory, realising the merit of putting the relativistic theory into an explicitly covariant form. He achieved this for the case of a two-body system by associating a different time variable with each of the particles. In response to questions raised by V A Fock, Dirac wrote a more general paper jointly with Fock and B Podolski, [15] which was published in a Russian journal, extending this procedure to many-particle systems, giving the so-called 'many-time formalism' of field theory which S Tomanaga made much use of a decade later in his fundamental work on the renormalisation of quantum electrodynamics. Dirac then published a further paper in the same journal, [16] again on the theme of explicit Lorentz invariance, but from a totally different viewpoint, making use of the Lagrangian rather than the Hamiltonian. The importance of this paper was not recognised at the time, but it proved to be of vital importance for Feynman in 1949 when he developed his Lorentz-covariant theory for the calculation of S-matrix amplitudes. Following Dirac's paper, Feynman was able to set up his 'sum-over-histories' formulation for theories of interacting fields, a formulation which was of central importance for the development of the S-matrix renormalisation programme, and which has been the starting point for the non-perturbative computer calculations of the implications of gauge field theories during the last few years.

Dirac was appointed to the Lucasian Professorship of Mathematics, Cambridge University, from 30 September 1932. It is noteworthy that this appointment followed only one year after the appointment of his former supervisor R H Fowler to the Plummer Chair of Mathematical Physics.

In 1933 Dirac was awarded the Nobel Prize for Physics, jointly with the Austrian E Schrödinger, for their development of quantum mechanics. In accepting this award, Dirac spoke especially

Paul Dirac in the front row (second left) at the Copenhagen Conference of 1933, with Niels Bohr on his right and Werner Heisenberg on his left.

about his relativistic equation for the electron and the resulting theory of the positron.

Dirac was well aware that the presence of a charged particle would perturb the negative energy states constituting the vacuum[17,18] and that this would call for a renormalisation of its charge. He also realised that, after such a renormalisation, there would be some finite effects left over, effects which we now characterise as vacuum polarisation and which could not be checked empirically until more than a decade later. Although Dirac's work consituted the first discussion of these effects, it turned out that the charge renormalisation needed was calculated to be infinite and Dirac was subsequently unwilling to accept these calculations as valid mathematics, not even for the finite vacuum polarisation terms which agree well with the empirical data.

1934–8

P Kapitza of the Cavendish Laboratory, Cambridge, a Russian national who had been working at Cambridge since 1921, and for whom the Mond Laboratory had been established as part of the Cavendish, made a visit to USSR in the early summer of 1934, and was prevented from returning on the grounds of national need. Dirac was very much perturbed by Kapitza's situation, which affected Dirac deeply for the rest of his life, and he soon visited Kapitza in Russia to give him moral support and to assess what the Royal Society and Cambridge University might be able to do to bring Kapitza back into productive research work. Dirac subsequently visited Kapitza each summer, until 1938 when the USSR government suspended the issue of visas by its London embassy for a time.

In the autumn of 1934 Dirac took up his first one-year appointment as Member of the Institute of Advanced Studies (IAS) at Princeton, New Jersey, on sabbatical leave from Cambridge University. He lectured regularly on quantum electrodynamics through both semesters of the 1934–5 academic year.

The second edition of *The Principles of Quantum Mechanics* was published in 1935. This was substantially longer than the first edition, with a good deal of change in the introductory chapters on fundamental principles and a new chapter on 'Field Theory' added at the end.

In the summer of 1936 Dirac joined Papalexi's Russian

expedition to observe the solar eclipse which was to reach totality in the Caucasus on 19 June. Unfortunately, Dirac's father died in Bristol on 15 June, and Dirac flew back from the Caucasus to attend the funeral which was held on 17 June. He subsequently returned to the Caucasus to take part in other activities he had planned there for July and August.

Paul Dirac, about 1935.

On 2 January 1937, at the Holborn Register Office, London, Dirac married Margit Balasz (née Wigner), the sister of his colleague Eugene Wigner, a physicist at Princeton University. Margit had two children, Gabriel and Judy, by a previous marriage, and they both adopted the surname Dirac. Dirac's stepson Gabriel became in time a student of Pure Mathematics at St John's College, and later a well known Professor of Pure Mathematics at the University of Aarhus, Denmark, until his death in 1984. Dirac moved out of St John's College and the family settled into a house at 7 Cavendish Avenue, Cambridge, which remained their principal residence until Dirac's retirement from the Lucasian Chair in 1969. Paul and Margit Dirac had two children, both girls. Mary Elizabeth, born in 1940, has married twice, most recently to P Tilley at Tallahassee in 1983. Florence Monica, born in 1942, studied geophysics at Oxford, and went on to take her PhD degree at Cambridge in 1971. She married R L Parker at Cambridge in 1968; she has one son, named Paul. Dirac's mother lived with the family in Cambridge towards the end of her life, and died there on 21 December 1941.

In 1938 Dirac focused his attention on the classical relativistic theory of the interaction of an electron with the electromagnetic field, including the electromagnetic field which it generates, i.e. including the effect of 'radiation reaction' on the motion of the electron.[20] He was led to a differential equation of third order in time derivatives and without infinities, but he found that it had unphysical properties, in particular so-called 'run-away' solutions, in which the electron accelerates indefinitely in response to its own radiation. The theory described a point electron but involved an explicit mass renormalisation. A mass renormalisation in the same spirit was later incorporated into the corresponding quantum electrodynamics, although this was never accepted as valid by Dirac.

1939–45

In 1939 Dirac was awarded the Royal Medal of the Royal Society. He was also elected an Honorary Member of the Indian Academy of Science. In 1941 Dirac delivered the Bakerian Lecture of the Royal Society, under the title 'On the interpretation of Quantum Mechanics'.[22]

During the war years, Dirac remained in Cambridge, carrying out his duties as Lucasian Professor, as well as fulfilling other roles in the university (e.g. as an examiner of first-year undergraduates) not usual for him but necessary because there were so few of the Mathematical Faculty staff still at Cambridge. Probably for the same reason, he undertook the supervision of a number of postgraduate research students from abroad, a responsibility he had generally been reluctant to accept in the 1930s; at the end of 1946, he was responsible for the research of four such students, C J Eliezer and S Shanmugadhasan from Ceylon (now Sri Lanka), S Ashauer from Brazil and Harish Chandra from India, all of whom took their PhD degrees in good time. During the war years he also did a good deal of consulting work for both Peierls's group at Birmingham (specifically on atomic bomb design and development, and also on the general problem of isotope separation) and Simon's group at the Clarendon Laboratory, Oxford (on the Dirac jet method for isotope separation, a process potentially of importance but in fact not needed before the end of the war).

In 1943 Dirac was elected Honorary Member of the Chinese Physical Society, and in 1944, of the Royal Irish Academy. He delivered some special lectures on quantum electrodynamics to the latter[23] in 1942 and lectured there again in 1945. In these years, Dirac developed the technique of using an indefinite metric in the formulation of a covariant theory. This was an important step, since it gave a secure basis for the procedure of using negative probabilities for non-physical states as a computational aid to simplify and abbreviate calculations, which had previously been possible only through non-covariant methods. His use of an indefinite metric later had a wide influence on the techniques used in field theory.

1946–53

In 1946, according to *The Times*, Dirac was made an honorary Doctor of Science of the University of Paris, apparently in his absence and without his acquiescence. In general, Dirac did not seek honours and replied 'regretfully, no' when any university sought to award him an honorary degree. Early in his career, he had rejected the offer of an honorary degree by his *alma mater*, the University of Bristol; having done so, he felt that he could not in good conscience accept an honorary degree from any other university.

Dirac visited IAS as Member for its 1946 Spring semester and Princeton University as Visiting Professor for the following Fall term, giving a lecture course on quantum electrodynamics at the latter. In 1946, he was also elected an Honorary Fellow of the Royal Society of Edinburgh, and in 1947, an Honorary Fellow of the National Institute of Sciences in India.

The third edition of *The Principles of Quantum Mechanics* was published in 1947. This introduced the bra and ket notation which pleased Dirac so much and separated the representation theory into two chapters, one dealing with discrete eigenvalues and the other

Paul Dirac lecturing in about 1946.

with continuous eigenvalues. The final chapter was lengthened and dealt primarily with quantum electrodynamics rather than with field theory in general.

For the academic year 1947–8 Dirac returned to IAS as Member, on sabbatical leave from Cambridge. While he was in America he was elected an Honorary Member of the American Physical Society. He continued his work of finding a proper form for relativistic field theory, developing a treatment based on a general space-like surface rather than on constant time surfaces, but working in Schrödinger representation. He also extended his work on magnetic monopoles.[24] Although Dirac later lost interest in this idea, since magnetic poles did not appear to exist in nature, his work on this topic was seminal, for it introduced into theoretical physics notions whose relevance physicists had previously been unaware of, and so led to a great deal of progress on new questions where these notions were appropriate and fruitful. This early work of Dirac has also been central to much work on grand unified field theories during the past decade, since these theories generally predict the existence of magnetic monopoles and it has been important to understand their role in these theories and the reasons for the apparent absence of magnetic monopoles in nature.

In 1949 he was elected a Foreign Associate of the US National Academy of Sciences, and in 1950, Foreign Honorary Member of the American Academy of Arts and Sciences. In 1951 he was elected a Member of Accademia delle Scienze di Torino, at Turin, Italy, and in 1953, a Member of Academia das Ciencias de Lisboa, at Lisbon, Portugal.

In September 1949 Dirac lectured on the relation of classical to quantum mechanics, a topic much on his mind during this period, at the Second Canadian Mathematical Congress, held on the campus of the University of British Columbia at Vancouver. This work led him on to a general discussion, through the following decade, of constrained dynamical systems and their quantisation by Hamiltonian methods. The methods he developed have proved to have widespread relevance today, since gauge theories necessarily involve such constraints and the theories under investigation now for the description of elementary particles and their interactions are all gauge theories.

In 1952 he was awarded the Copley Medal of the Royal Society, their senior award. Earlier in the same year he had been awarded the third 'Max Planck' Medal, the first two having been awarded long before to Planck and to Einstein, by the Association of German Physics Institutes and the Max Planck Foundation.

1954–5

Dirac took this academic year as sabbatical leave, having received an invitation from J R Oppenheimer, then Director of IAS, to spend this year as Member of his Institute. However, it was announced by the US State Department on 26 May 1954 that it had refused to issue a visa for him to enter the USA, no reason being given. Dirac speculated that the cause probably lay in the series of nine visits he had made to the USSR before World War II, to attend scientific conferences, but noted that he had already been given an entry visa to the USA on three earlier occasions after the war.

At short notice, Dirac made other plans for his sabbatical year. He visited the Tata Institute of Fundamental Research at Bombay for the first half of this year, giving a course of lectures on quantum mechanics and relativistic field theory there which the Institute subsequently published. The Dirac family then travelled by ship to Japan and thence to Canada, where Dirac took up a visiting research appointment at the National Research Council, Ottawa. During the first leg of this voyage, Dirac suffered a serious illness (hepatitis) which persisted and put him straight into hospital on his arrival at Vancouver. He recovered only slowly from this illness in the subsequent months.

1955–67

In 1955 Dirac accepted a Visiting Professorship at Moscow University and gave lectures there in the autumn, both to the students at the university and to other professional bodies in Moscow. When asked at the university to write briefly his philosophy of physics, he wrote on the blackboard

'PHYSICAL LAWS SHOULD HAVE MATHEMATICAL BEAUTY'

and this has been preserved there to this day.

Paul Dirac at the Lindau Meeting of 1959.

During this period, his mind continued to be occupied by questions about the Hamiltonian formalism, especially for the theory of gravitation, with quantisation of the gravitational field as an ultimate objective.

A fourth edition of *The Principles of Quantum Mechanics* appeared in 1957. The last chapter, entitled 'Quantum Electrodynamics' in the third edition, was completely rewritten, emphasising the role of electron–positron pair creation and annihilation and abandoning the analogy of classical electrodynamics on which the earlier treatment was based.

In 1958 he was elected a Member of the Deutsche Akademie der Naturforscher Leopoldina, at Halle, GDR, and a Member of Accademia Nazionale dei Lincei, at Rome. In 1961 he was appointed as Member of the Pontifical Academy of Sciences, Vatican City, and in 1962 as Member of Kongelige Danske Videnskabernes Selskab (Royal Danish Academy of Sciences and Letters) at Copenhagen. He visited IAS again as Member for its academic years 1958–9 and 1962–3. He also spent a sabbatical year 1963–4 at Yeshiva University, New York City, where he lectured on quantum mechanics and on quantum field theory, the latter bringing together his work on the Hamiltonian treatment of constrained dynamical systems. Both sets of lecture notes appeared later as printed books. In 1966 he was awarded an honorary doctorate by Moscow University, again in his absence. He spent March and April of 1966 as Visiting Professor at the Institute of Theoretical Physics of the State University of New York at Stony Brook. He returned to the same position for three weeks in the spring of 1967, and again for three weeks in December 1968.

In 1967, a revised fourth edition of *The Principles of Quantum Mechanics* appeared, the changes being confined to the chapter on quantum electrodynamics, the last section 'Difficulties of the Theory' being replaced by two sections entitled 'Interpretation' and 'Applications'.

1968–72

Early in 1968, Dirac spent two months at the Center for Theoretical Studies (CTS), University of Miami, Coral Gables, Florida, as Visiting Member. In 1969 he was awarded the first J Robert Oppenheimer Prize of the University of Miami, and he lectured at CTS on 'The basic ideas of quantum mechanics' for the first three months of that year, holding the same appointment again. After he returned to Cambridge, he retired from his Lucasian Professorship on 30 September 1969, at the statutory retirement age.

Dirac retired to the USA, where so many of his friends lived.

Early in 1970 he spent several months at CTS as Visiting Member. Later in that year, he took up an appointment as Visiting Eminent Professor at the Florida State University (FSU), Tallahassee, for four months from September to December, after which he went on to CTS again, as Visiting Member. In 1971 he accepted and took up in September the appointment as Research Professor at FSU which he held until his death.

Paul Dirac at the Lindau Meeting of 1971. His brother-in-law Eugene Wigner is in the foreground.

During this period he continued research on a wide range of topics, especially on the possible time dependence of the fundamental constants, but also on mathematical topics he found interesting. In 1972 a conference was held at the International Centre for Theoretical Physics at Trieste, to celebrate Dirac's seventieth birthday and a congratulatory volume entitled 'Aspects of Symmetry' edited by A Salam and E P Wigner and reviewing all the areas of his major contributions to physics, was prepared for it.

1973–84

In 1973 Dirac was awarded the Order of Merit, an outstanding recognition by the land of his birth. In this period, he spoke many times on matters of historical interest concerning quantum mechanics, although always reluctantly for he did not like to spend his time on matters he did not consider of importance for physics. He also wrote quite a number of articles, scientific biographies or on questions of cosmology, for *Commentarii*, the publication of the Pontifical Academy of Sciences. He attended the triennial Lindau Conferences regularly and generally spoke there on some topic currently of interest to him.

Paul Dirac at the 1973 Lindau Meeting. Werner Heisenberg is standing immediately behind him.

In August and September 1975 he visited Australia and New Zealand, giving five lectures in each country, which were later collected together in book form.

A conference was held at FSU in 1976 in his honour, on the Measurement of Cosmological Variations of the Gravitational Constant, an interest which he actively pursued in his last years, developing its philosophy and precise form as the empirical evidence grew and improved. In 1978 he gave the first H R Crane Lecture at the University of Michigan, on the prediction of antimatter.

Peter Kapitza and Paul Dirac in deep discussion at the lunch table during the Lindau Meeting of 1979. (Photograph by Hans Rotta.)

Professor Dirac at the Lindau Meeting of 1982.

From 1969, the year of his first connection with CTS, he spoke regularly at the Coral Gables Conference (later named Orbis Scientiae), usually giving the opening scientific lecture. Right to the end, Dirac was firmly opposed to the doctrine of renormalisation in field theory, and this was the topic of his last talk at Orbis Scientiae in January 1983. Although visibly failing, he spoke clearly and firmly, albeit softly, and the lecture he gave is scheduled for

Pencil sketch of Paul Dirac made by R Tollast in 1963, now on the wall of the Senior Tutor's office, St John's College, Cambridge.

publication in a book to be published by Cambridge University Press in 1987, edited by B Kursunoglu and E P Wigner and entitled *The Dirac Memorial Volume*, which was to commemorate his eightieth birthday but which will instead be a memorial volume to him.

Professor Paul Adrien Maurice Dirac, OM, FRS, died at Tallahassee on 20 October 1984 and was buried in Tallahassee cemetery.

Acknowledgments

The photographs on pp. 13, 15, 18, 20, 22, 23 and 24 are reproduced from an article by H B G Casimir in *Naturwissenschaftliche Rundschau* **38** (1985) by kind permission of the publishers and author.

References

A select list of 24 major papers by Dirac

1   1925 The fundamental equations of quantum mechanics *Proc. R. Soc.* A **109** 642–53
2   1926 Quantum mechanics and a preliminary investigation of the hydrogen atom *Proc. R. Soc.* A **110** 561–79
3   1926 On quantum algebra *Proc. Camb. Phil. Soc.* **23** 412–18
4   1926 On the theory of quantum mechanics *Proc. R. Soc.* A **112** 661–77
5   1927 The physical interpretation of the quantum dynamics *Proc. R. Soc.* A **113** 621–41
6   1927 The quantum theory of emission and absorption of radiation *Proc. R. Soc.* A **114** 243–65
7   1927 The quantum theory of dispersion *Proc. R. Soc.* A **114** 710–28
8   1928 The quantum theory of the electron *Proc R. Soc.* A **117** 610–24

9 1928 The quantum theory of the electron II *Proc. R. Soc. A* **118** 351–61

10 1929 The basis of statistical quantum mechanics *Proc. Camb. Phil. Soc.* **25** 62–6

11 1930 A theory of electrons and protons *Proc. R. Soc. A* **126** 360–5

12 1930 On the annihilation of electrons and protons *Proc. Camb. Phil. Soc.* **26** 361–75

13 1931 Quantized singularities in the electromagnetic field *Proc. R. Soc. A* **133** 60–72

14 1932 Relativistic quantum mechanics *Proc. R. Soc. A* **136** 453–64

15 1932 On quantum electrodynamics (with V A Fock and B Podolski) *Phys. Z. der Sowjetunion* **2** 468–79

16 1933 The Lagrangian in quantum mechanics *Phys. Z. der Sowjetunion* **3** 64–72

17 1933 Théorie du positron *Septiéme Conseil de Physique Solvay (Structure et Propriétés des Noyaux Atomiques), 22–29 October 1933* (Paris: Gauthier-Villars, 1934)

18 1934 Discussion of the infinite distribution of electrons in the theory of the positron *Proc. Camb. Phil. Soc.* **30** 150–63

19 1936 Relativistic wave equations *Proc. R. Soc. A* **155** 447-59

20 1938 Classical theory of radiating electrons *Proc. R. Soc. A* **167** 148–69

21 1939 La théorie de l'électron et du champ éléctromagnetique *Ann. Inst. H. Poincaré* **9** 13–49

22 1941 The physical interpretation of quantum mechanics (Bakerian Lecture 1941) *Proc. R. Soc. A* **180** 1–40

23 1943 Quantum electrodynamics *Comm. Dublin Inst. Adv. Stud.* ser. A no 1

24 1948 The theory of magnetic poles *Phys. Rev.* **74** 817–30

Books published by Dirac

1930 *The Principles of Quantum Mechanics* (Oxford: Clarendon)

1935 *The Principles of Quantum Mechanics* 2nd edn (a re-written and expanded text) (Oxford: Clarendon)

1947 *The Principles of Quantum Mechanics* 3rd edn (a revised text) (Oxford: Clarendon)

1958 *The Principles of Quantum Mechanics* 4th edn (a further revised text) (Oxford: Clarendon) (further revised 1967)

1964 *Lectures on Quantum Mechanics* (Yeshiva University, New York: Belfer Graduate School of Science)

1966 *Lectures on Quantum Field Theory* (Yeshiva University, New York: Belfer Graduate School of Science)

1974 *Spinors in Hilbert Space* (New York: Plenum)

1975 *General Theory o｡˘ Relativity* (New York: Wiley-Interscience)

1978 *Directions in Physics* eds H Hora and J R Shepanski (New York: Wiley-Interscience)

Part 1

Personal Reminiscences

Some Words from a Former Student

R J N Phillips

It is a privilege to be allowed a few moments of reminiscence and of tribute to the man whom we have gathered to honour.

I was fortunate to be Professor Dirac's student during 1954. It happened rather by accident. We were all — my contemporaries and I — immensely in awe of the Great Man. We had bought his book and had sat in his Part III lecture course on quantum mechanics (a severe culture shock, as those who took it will remember) but I would not have dared to ask him to supervise my research. After about a year, however, he happened to be one of the judges for the Smiths Prize essay competition, which I had entered. Mine was an undistinguished effort, but it chanced to be on a problem that had interested him, namely putting the Tomonaga–Schwinger equation into the Schrödinger representation. A little while later I received a discreet message through my supervisor that Dirac would be prepared to have me as a student.

And so it was arranged that I should go to see him once a week at his office in the Arts School; I believe it may have been 10 o'clock on Tuesdays. On the first of these occasions he gave me some reprints to read. Taking them home I was mortified to discover that he had already solved the whole problem (and much else beside) with great power and generality several years before and had published it all in the *Canadian Journal of Mathematics*.[1] Next week I was full of apologies for not knowing about this work and volunteered that my essay had totally mismanaged the integrability conditions. With that fleeting smile that everyone will recall, he agreed that he had noticed this — but then went on to more positive things. He was a kind and gentle person as I remember, sparing of words, preferring people to read and understand for themselves but willing to explain where necessary. I believe he took me on simply to rescue something from my previous mistaken efforts.

At the end of that summer Dirac left Cambridge for a sabbatical leave and I finished my time with someone else. It was an exceptional privilege to have been his student, but indeed we were all privileged who studied beside him. His work and achievements set superlative standards, while his unassuming presence among us was an encouragement along the way. We shall not see such days again.

Note

1 Dirac P A M *Can. J. Math.* **2** 129 (1950) and **3** 1 (1951)

A Brief Reminiscence of Dirac

J C Polkinghorne

Like many generations of Cambridge students, my first acquaintance with Paul Dirac was through his famous lecture course on quantum mechanics. It followed his book closely and was exceptionally clear, elegant and authoritative. One was carried along in the unfolding of an argument which seemed as majestically inevitable as the development of the theme of a fugue by J S Bach. It was a great thrill for a young man to know that he was learning quantum mechanics 'straight from the horse's mouth', from one of the subject's founding fathers. The course conveyed in a powerful way the great beauty of fundamental thought in theoretical physics. But the most striking thing about the lectures was the self-effacement of the lecturer. Paul Dirac made no attempt whatsoever to draw attention to the many and substantial contributions which he had made to the subject. I found such natural and graceful humility most impressive.

Later, as a graduate student, I attended the weekly theoretical physics seminar held in Room F of the Arts School. It was a curious setting, for the room was lined with display cabinets full of plaster models of ruled surfaces and the like, the impedimenta of the geometrical interests of many years ago. There were three large easy chairs, occupied by Nick Kemmer, Jim Hamilton and, of course, Paul Dirac. The rest of us perched on distinctly uncomfortable seating round the edge of the room. Dirac settled into his chair and, to a casual observer, might have seemed soon overcome with somnolence. However, he would occasionally open an eye and put a penetrating and unexpected question to the speaker. One was conscious of an alert and powerful intellect.

33

I suppose that Dirac was the most intellectually impressive person I have had the privilege of knowing — not a statement made lightly by a Fellow of Trinity. I am very grateful to have sat at his feet and been his colleague.

Address to Dirac Memorial Meeting, Cambridge

Rudolf Peierls

This is really a family gathering, since theoretical physicists still are like a family. By now they are a very large family, of which only a small part is here today. We have gathered to commemorate one of the greatest members of the family, perhaps the greatest in our lifetime. The nature of his greatness has been brought out very clearly this afternoon; tonight we are thinking of him as a person.

I remember him in this dining hall in the 1930s, but this was not the first time I met him. He visited Leipzig in 1928 to give a lecture†, which was mentioned this afternoon, and as a very young graduate student I was detailed to take him to the theatre. I do not remember what was the play we saw, or what was his reaction to it, but I remember being terribly worried by his refusal to part with his hat. It was then obligatory in German theatres to leave hats and coats in the cloakroom. It was summer, and we wore no overcoats, but Dirac kept his hat, as was the custom in England. I worried all through the evening about the disastrous consequences that would follow, but of course nothing happened.

His visit to Leipzig was one of his many journeys. He was an inveterate traveller. The story is told how he arrived at the Russian border with a visa valid for a different entry point, and had to wait some days in a miserable little border village for the paperwork to be sorted out. There was not always time to learn the language of the countries he was visiting, but the first words that he wanted to know in a new country were how to ask for a glass of water. He

† [See Dalitz's Biographical Sketch.]

never took to alcoholic drinks. A colleague who noticed this, and the fact that he did not smoke, asked him whether he had any vices. 'No obvious ones' was Paul's reply.

People called him very taciturn, but he could be very articulate when he had something to say — he just did not make idle conversation. When he did speak, his remarks were often surprising to his listeners, but this was because he did not have the trivial associations which deflect most of us from a completely logical course; he would always follow a thought to its logical consequences. This is of course very noticeable in his papers, but there were many examples outside physics. On one social occasion in Cambridge it was noted with surprise that all children born recently to physicists had been girls, and someone said 'It must be something in the air.' After a pause, Dirac added 'Or in the water.'

He also did not share common prejudices. At a time when everything Russian was anathema, he questioned why each particular item was regarded as wrong, and this often caused raised eyebrows.

He could surprise us in other ways. One of the great surprises for his friends was his marriage to a lady (whom we welcome among us here tonight) who seemed so completely different from him in almost every way.

It was surprising to see the serious interest he took in domestic affairs, including the garden. He was a keen gardener, and tried to deal with horticultural problems from first principles, which did not always lead to good results.

The many topics outside quantum mechanics which attracted his interest included isotope separation. He not only thought about the theory, but carried out experiments. In fact he invented a method of isotope separation, and tried to make it work, using equipment put at his disposal by Kapitza. This work was abandoned when, in 1934, Kapitza failed to return from Moscow. The idea was revived during the war, when isotope separation acquired great practical importance, and a group in Oxford showed that the method was workable. They received much sound practical advice from Paul. The project was not pursued because other methods appeared to be more economical.

His general ideas about isotope separation became very useful to the work on atomic energy during the war. In unpublished notes he introduced the notions of 'separating power' and 'separation potential', which are now used generally, and help to simplify the discussion of plant design.

He also took an interest in other aspects of atomic energy work. In the course of time these contacts stopped. I believe this was because he was beginning to feel that atom bombs were not a matter he wanted to be associated with, and who would blame him?

When he was awarded the Nobel Prize he told Rutherford that he did not want to accept it because he disliked publicity. Rutherford said 'A refusal will get you much more publicity', and then he accepted.

But he would never compromise his principles and would stick absolutely to what he saw as right. No doubt the best comment on him was the remark by Niels Bohr: 'Of all physicists, Dirac has the purest soul.'

With this I would ask you to drink to the memory of Paul Dirac.

Reminiscences at the Dinner held at St John's College

Bertha Jeffreys (Swirles)

I think that I have been asked to speak this evening because I am one of the few people still alive who attended Paul Dirac's first lecture course in the Easter term of 1926. I see, as clearly as I see you now, a sunny morning, and Ralph Fowler and Douglas Hartree walking across the court over there and Hartree saying to someone he met, 'We have been listening to the great man Dirac.' I am sure that we all realised his very special quality. He worked on *fundamental* problems, not minor ones. The lectures were clear and completely characteristic in style and I think it is because of hearing him then that when I read anything of his I hear him saying it.

The first time I heard him lecture was at a Cavendish colloquium giving an account of Born's 'Quantenmechanik der Stoszvorgänge' paper, and quite honestly it was not very good, but he can have had very little time to prepare it. You must understand that the meeting place for theoretical physicists in those days was just the very small library in the old Cavendish and this didn't tend to sociability. Fowler was supervisor to all of us and we went to see him in his rooms in Trinity.

I confess that in the later part of the summer of 1926 I found the Schrödinger papers more digestible. Matrices and non-commutative algebra had not been part of my education. In the winter of 1927–8 when I was in Göttingen, Fowler wrote that Dirac had something very exciting and this was the relativistic paper.

In March 1929 when I was an assistant lecturer in the Mathematics Department at Manchester we were having an examiners' meeting and Dirac was due to give a lecture later in the afternoon. I think Fowler must have been there as he was external examiner. A porter came and announced that Mrs Dirac had arrived. This occasioned some surprise but then we learned that it was his mother. Afterwards the Mordells gave a dinner party and then I took Mrs Dirac to the railway station as she had to get back to Bristol that night. I understood that Mr Dirac was disabled and that she had to help him. I suspect that I must have taken her on foot and by tram as they were my means of transport in those days.

I have a rather uncharacteristic story. It has been mentioned that Dirac was an early traveller to Russia after the Revolution. Many years later in 1958 we were going to the International Astronomical Union meeting in Moscow and at some party I said to Dirac that I was not sure that I liked caviar, to which he replied that there was not much point in going to Russia if one didn't like caviar.

I do commend to those that have not seen it Dirac's own 'Recollections of an Exciting Era', given at the Varenna Summer School in 1972.

Notes added 6 September 1985

I have verified from my lecture notes that Fowler and Dirac often lectured on the same morning. Fowler's lectures were mainly on the most recent work on theory of atomic spectra. From the Cambridge University *Reporter* for 1925–6, I see that in October and January the title of Dirac's Easter term course was 'Quantum Theory of Specific Heats'; in April it was 'Quantum Mechanics (Recent Developments)'. A quotation from my notes is 'It turns out to be a Poisson bracket (everything does for this purpose as it is the only thing you can interpret).' At the beginning he gave just the references to the 1924 and 1925 papers of Einstein and Bose, but the substance of the course was his own and Heisenberg's recent work.

Address delivered to Memorial Meeting in Tallahassee†

Eugene Wigner

It is a great pleasure to recall contacts with Paul, both the scientific and the personal ones. But it is painful to realise that personal contacts will not occur anymore and that, in the future, we can enjoy only learning more about his scientific ideas — his person will be permanently absent.

I will talk mostly about my early contacts with Paul and I hope those of you who are not physicists will forgive me for describing some of his accomplishments in the area of physics — those which impressed me most. The first one of these which is most vividly in my mind came when I was in Göttingen and tried, in collaboration with Pascual Jordan, to find a relativistic quantum equation for the electron. We worked hard and had several ideas, but were not fully satisfied with any of them. Then our boss, Professor Born, received a letter from Paul. The letter described Paul's obligations for the coming months — but there was a postscript of about four lines. These four lines gave his relativistic quantum equation of the electron; four lines of extreme simplicity, but giving his ingenious and convincing idea very clearly.

Professor Born showed the letter to my collaborator Jordan and he was overwhelmed. He told me that he was sorry we did not have Paul's wonderful idea, but it is good that somebody had it. And our admiration for his imaginative approach increased the already great respect which we had for his thinking. As the physicists

† [19 November 1984, Tallahassee, Florida.]

40

among you know, this became Paul's most famous paper — even though, I believe, another one introducing the quantum field, had an even greater and more lasting effect.

But this was not a personal contact for me and the first truly personal ones came much later in the course of my half-yearly stays in Princeton when a one-term visit of his coincided with mine. Both of us had a room rented for our visit and we got our meals outside. Somehow we got accustomed to having our meals together; we talked a great deal about physics even though he liked to say something about our science only if he had something truly important to say. But he often had, and not only about physics, but also about transferring information, giving lectures, suggesting and answering questions after the lecture. I enjoyed attending his lectures, enjoyed them even if I was already familiar with the subject, enjoyed also his answers to the questions after the lectures. And he told me that he also enjoyed answering questions.

I just told you about our usual meals together, but I will tell you now about a very important one. On my 1934 visit to Princeton, my sister came along with me and we went out for a luncheon. As we ate, Paul, who had arrived the evening before, happened to enter the same restaurant and appeared to be greatly surprised as he saw the two of us. My sister Manci [Margit Wigner] noticed this and she asked me who that was who had just come in. When I looked and noticed Paul, I told her about the earlier meals Paul and I had together, and when she heard about them, she encouraged me to invite him to join us for the luncheon. I did, and this introduced, in due course of time, a happy marriage.

And I am proud to have contributed to the existence of that marriage!

Let me mention one more personal event from Paul's life. During the war Paul, as were many others, was greatly concerned not only about the future of England, but also that of the whole world, of freedom, democracy and a diversity of cultures. When Hitler attacked the western part of Europe, and in particular also England, he volunteered to do scientific and technical work for the defence of his country and the freedom of the world. What is very memorable in this connection is that he considered this to be his duty and refused all compensation for his work. I must admit that I do not know the special subject he worked on — it seems to have been a secret — but the fact that he did it so unselfishly, as a gift to freedom, is worth remembering. And the Free World, as we now have some of it, has a proud recollection of Paul Adrien Maurice Dirac. His wife Margit is also justly proud of it. So are many of us!

Eulogy for Paul A M Dirac 19 November 1984: 'Who Was This Guy?'

J E Lannutti

A few weeks ago, at the cemetery, after Paul's funeral service, after most people had left, a young *Tallahassee Democrat* reporter asked me, 'who was this guy?' I made some terse remark about checking his files. But, 'who was this guy?' I had in mind only the answer: 'he was Paul A M Dirac!' Of course, to a young reporter that was not enough. But it was impossible to say in a few sentences what would appropriately characterise the life of this internationally acclaimed intellectual giant.

We have heard and read much about Paul the great scientist—Nobel laureate, Member of the Order of Merit, Member of the Papal Academy of Science, the US National Academy of Science, the Soviet Academy of Science, the Royal Society, the Indian Academy of Science and the Hungarian Academy of Science. The list of his awards is endless. But how do I remember him? It depends on the situation.

In most social interactions he was mild-mannered, gentle, soft-spoken, reticent, modest, concise, restrained, unobtrusive, reserved and unpretentious. Personally, he was self-disciplined, strong-willed, resolute, firm, self-reliant, independent, persevering, stubborn and tireless. In his intellectual work he was meticulous, mathematically and scientifically exact, rigorous, concise, honest, clear-thinking, courageous, self-sufficient and tenacious.

Memories can be recyled at will and we all have memories about Paul the person. The most salient feature of Paul internationally was his concise and precise manner of speech. The stories are legion, some are probably apocryphal. For example after a Dirac lecture, the session chairman asked the audience if they had any questions. A person stood up and said 'I did not understand the derivation of ... etc, etc.' Paul made no response, the chairman asked, 'aren't you going to answer the question?' Paul said, 'that was a statement, not a question.'

Although my knowledge and appreciation of Paul Dirac began in the childhood of my career in physics, I had never seen or heard him speak until the first time he came to visit Florida State in January 1970. If I remember correctly, someone had met him at one of Behram Kursunoglu's conferences in Miami and invited him to visit.

I remember being emotionally moved by that first colloquium. Having studied and worked in physics for many years, the name Dirac was a basic constituent, an integral part of the warp and woof of my understanding of physics. Dirac was not a person. Dirac was an equation, a theory of antimatter, a δ-function, a monopole or a kind of statistics. He was only a name in textbooks and history—in association with other great names such as Einstein, Schrödinger, Heisenberg and Bohr. But, now, he was here, in person! Describing his work and his interactions with our other heroes in textbooks!

My experience was not unusual. I have learned that it had occurred with almost everyone at Dirac lectures—always given to capacity crowds.

Having NSF science development funds budgeted for visiting eminent professors, we invited him to come back for the Fall semester. He agreed! We were elated! He spent the Fall of 1970 with us.

About a week before the Diracs were to leave, at a Christmas party at my home, Margit Dirac took me aside to say that Paul liked it here. She asked if it would be possible to arrange a continuing appointment. I calmly responded that I would investigate. Of course, what I couldn't say was, that this was what we were hoping for all along!

Within two days after a sequence of meetings with Norman Heydenberg (our department Chairman), Bob Lawton (Dean of Arts and Sciences), Paul Craig (Vice President for Academic Affairs), Stan Marshall (President) and Bob Mautz (Chancellor), Paul was given an offer and he accepted.

I especially remember that, since Bob Lawton was a Shakespeare scholar, he became more enthusiastic when I asked how he would respond if Shakespeare had asked to join our faculty!

The next 14 years are a kaleidoscope of memories and I will recite only a few personal ones.

Lunch on the seventh floor with Paul, Steve Edwards and Bill Moulton.

Paul walking to work every day.

Getting him on our high energy physics Department of Energy contract to support him with a research associate and a graduate student.

Comment by our DOE contract monitor concerning the need for peer review of the research proposal: 'Who could be a peer to Dirac? whose opinion could he accept, if contrary?'

His refusal to accept an honorary degree from FSU since he had consistently refused every other university in the world and he did not want to insult them.

His contention at a mathematics department seminar that the mathematics that applies in physics must be beautiful, since it was the form selected by God.

The female undergraduate student who came to his office and handed him a single rose. Commenting only that it was to respect and honour him, and then leaving without introduction.

My first non-family visitors after my heart surgery were Paul and Margit—Paul's strong recommendation was that I do more walking for exercise.

Then, for more than a year, walking with Paul four to ten miles on the forest fire trails of the Appalachicola National Forest each Saturday and Sunday — Lost Lake, Dog Lake, Silver Lake, behind the Aenon church, around Lake Bradford, etc contemplating nature from a lakeside.

Recounting his experiences as an air-raid warden during World War II

Paul being prompted by Margit to tell jokes at teas in the Dirac living room.

Paul avoiding medical doctors — until an introduction to Hank and Henrietta Watt began a lasting friendship. Hank subsequently became of tremendous importance to Paul and Margit.

Paul's smile and sparkle when I visited him in his office.

His desk full of letters from people seeking his opinion. Once complaining that people should have the courage and commitment to proceed with their ideas themselves.

Surprise of an *Encyclopaedia Britannica* interviewer when Paul said that the physics departments at Cambridge and Florida State were about the same quality.

Recounting his defence of North Florida water resources at a meeting with the Governor.

His greatest fear was loss of intellectual prowess. But he continued to be creative to the end, dictating a contribution for a Kapitza Memorial Volume to his research associate, Leopold Halpern, a few days before he died.

Even with a severe case of flu, because he had promised, he travelled to Fermilab near Chicago and stood alone on a stage in front of an auditorium full of physicists and talked continuously for two hours without rest, reciting historical anecdotes for a conference on the history of physics.

His unusual and unique agreement to let us use his name on the main road for Innovation Park. Evidence of his strong support for his adopted community! He very much wanted to help Innovation Park and Florida State.

Although he was one of the fathers of quantum mechanics, he contended that it was wrong, and young physicists should not accept it so readily without question.

His grand programmes continued to the end. The gravitational strength is not constant, he said, and there are observable cosmological consequences. The pathological representations of the Lorentz group may hold clues for a new quantum mechanics, he said.

'Who was this guy?' he was Paul A M Dirac! World leader in science. Profoundly influential in the course of science and history. Acquaintance of Einstein, Queen Elizabeth II and the Pope. Known and respected worldwide. Honoured, by academies of science throughout the world. A modest and gentle human being. Probably Tallahassee's greatest ever resident.

An intellectual giant who lived and worked with us for almost fourteen years. Uplifting and honouring us. His spirit lives on through his friends and his intellectual legacies. His body rests among us forever. This man made a difference!

Dirac as Research Supervisor and Other Remembrances

S Shanmugadhasan

Dirac's postgraduate students and research associates 1944–55

After C J Eliezer left Cambridge in the summer of 1943, Miss S Ashauer and a Chinese student (both sponsored by the British Council) arrived in Cambridge in Michaelmas term 1944 to work under Dirac. But towards the end of Lent term 1945 the Chinese student transferred to experimental physics at the Cavendish Laboratory because, as he himself told me, he was having difficulty with the papers Dirac had asked him to study. I became Dirac's student in Lent term 1945. Harish-Chandra came in Michaelmas term 1945, but Dirac accepted him only after some delay. Because of previous published work under H J Bhabha, Harish-Chandra could complete his PhD in two years and left Cambridge for Princeton in the summer of 1947. Both Miss Ashauer and I completed our dissertations by the end of Michaelmas term 1947. Dirac was away from Cambridge during Michaelmas term 1946 at some celebration at Princeton University, and again during the academic year 1947–8 at the Institute for Advanced Study, Princeton. L Gårding spent a postdoctoral year in Cambridge during the academic year 1944–5. His doctoral thesis in Sweden was on group representations, and so he used to have conversations with Dirac on the subject. From Michaelmas term 1945 to the summer of 1947, T S Chang, who had obtained his PhD under R H Fowler, was back in Cambridge under British Council auspices, and was in contact with Dirac. R J Eden became Dirac's student in Michaelmas term 1948. H J D Cole was the next student, but he seems to have left after a year or so. In Easter term 1951 I met an

American student, B H McCormick, who was under Dirac's supervision, but he too seems to have left early. S F J Tyabji worked under Dirac for three years, beginning in Michaelmas term 1951.

Dirac was usually very reluctant to supervise research students. For instance, H Samara was a research student under A H Wilson (now Sir Alan) during the academic year 1944–5. When Wilson left Cambridge in the summer of 1945, Samara thought that Dirac would take him on. No, Samara had to wait for Wilson's successor. Harish-Chandra has told me that Dirac at first did not want to supervise him either, but acquiesced only after repeated requests from the Degree Committee. Miss Ashauer told me that at their first meeting Dirac informed her that he did not have a problem for her but that A H Wilson had one ready and so perhaps they should go and see Wilson. It seems he repeated it on a later occasion. But both times, in her innocence, she did not react to Dirac's suggestion. Only later, after she knew more about Dirac's ways, did it occur to her that Dirac was probably trying to hand her over to Wilson. After knowing all this, I have often wondered about my good fortune. My college tutor (the late Mr W L Cuttle) knew that Dirac was my first preference. So my guess is that he used his influence with the Degree Committee to secure Dirac for me.

Dirac as research supervisor
After his appointment as supervisor, Dirac did not call me to see him. I had to make the first move. (In Michaelmas and Lent terms one could see him by waiting outside his room at the Arts School just after his lectures on quantum mechanics. During Easter term and the vacations, if he was in Cambridge, he was usually available in his room on Saturday mornings.) At our first meeting, Dirac asked me what I had been doing. At H J Bhabha's suggestion I had been working on a minor problem on M Mathisson's variational equation of relativistic dynamics, which was related to Dirac's approach to the classical theory of radiating electrons. In fact, Dirac had prepared Mathisson's second paper for publication in volume 38 of the *Proceedings of the Cambridge Philosophical Society* (1942) after Mathisson's premature death. After listening to my report, he asked for my notes so that he could go over them later. At our next meeting he said that my work seemed all right and suggested that I should speak about Mathisson's work and my work at the colloquium right after him. The colloquia had just been

resumed, and Dirac was the opening speaker on his work and the related work of Bhabha and Harish-Chandra. During that term I did a little more work on my problem and showed my results to Dirac. He then told me to write up my results in the form of a paper. After the manuscript was ready, I asked Dirac what I should do next. He suggested a subject that was a natural continuation of the work just completed. He hastened to warn me (twice, in fact) that he did not even know whether the problem was solvable. But he emphasised that it was worth thinking about. Thus he gave me a difficult task and he expected me to tackle it on my own. A preliminary part was easy to do. But the main part was a different story. I was getting dejected that there had been no real progress at all after three months. It was time to report my failure to Dirac. I described some of my attempts; he asked me whether I had tried one or two other possibilities. Indeed I had, and I mentioned a few more unsuccessful tacks. Finally he said to me: 'You have been doing very well with your problem so far. You know, this is the kind of problem for which one does not even know whether a solution exists. One keeps thinking and thinking about the problem until suddenly one day one comes up with the right solution. And then one realises what a fool one has been for not thinking of it in the first place.' These words of encouragement, coming from Dirac, lifted my spirits and spurred me to persevere for a few more months until one day I hit upon a solution. (Some years later I found that H A Kramers had done some work in the same direction several years earlier.) Dirac approved the solution and asked me to write it up in the form of a paper. On returning my manuscript, he wondered whether I could not make the presentation more attractive. I replied that I needed specific hints or suggestions. Dirac did not offer any, and so the paper was sent to a journal without change. Again I asked Dirac what I should do next. He suggested that I should treat a specific application of the equations just obtained. I carried out the calculation by two methods developed by Dirac. The second method, developed only a few years before, was not yielding the right result. This discrepancy aroused his interest and he thought about it for a few days. Then he pointed out that I was overlooking a certain property in doing my calculation. That step overcame the difficulty. He wanted me to display the formulae in graphs and then write up a paper. In Easter term 1947 I asked Dirac whether he minded my not submitting my dissertation in Michaelmas term 1947 so as to continue my research uninterrupted. He replied that I had more than enough work for my dissertation and that, if I did not submit my dissertation at that time, the university might think I was a weak candidate.

From L Infeld's book *Quest: The Evolution of a Scientist* (1941) I knew that Dirac would be an unusual supervisor and that one should not expect too much help from him in doing one's research. So in general I went to him only when I had to consult him: to get subjects for research, to show him my results, or to report my failures. He indicated what subjects to investigate. But you were expected to work as much as possible on your own and not lean too much on him. (He explicitly confirmed this to me in the 1950s.) He did not even give any guidance on the relevant literature. But he looked through my results. And he gave encouragement when I needed it. Despite his sink or swim attitude towards his students, I firmly believed that Dirac was the best kind of supervisor one could have. So I was quite surprised to hear stories to the contrary from other students. Even V F Weisskopf has noted in 1971 that Dirac was of no help to him. [1]

Miss Ashauer told me that Dirac suggested her research problems too. She saw him more often than I did. When she was stuck in her work, she would take her difficulties to him and he did help in resolving them. On one occasion he directed her to consult an appropriate mathematician about some mathematical point. Another time he asked her not to mention his name so many times in a paper of hers. When she reported a mistake she had found in her earlier calculations, Dirac commented: 'Everyone makes mistakes. But the important thing is to catch them oneself before somebody else does.' Miss Ashauer's British Council scholarship could not be extended beyond Easter term 1947 because it would then exceed the maximum limit; so her college told her to try for a college scholarship or fellowship by submitting a dissertation. When the result was known, Dirac wanted to know whether it was a scholarship or fellowship.

When Harish-Chandra approached Dirac for a problem, Dirac asked him to come back the next day. Then Dirac suggested that Harish-Chandra should extend Dirac's recent work on the unitary representations of the Lorentz group to half-integral spins. Earlier, at the Colloquium at the Dublin Institute for Advanced Studies in July 1945, Dirac had mentioned that he had given the same problem to L Gårding but that he had not heard anything from Gårding. Harish-Chandra solved the problem very quickly and took his solution to Dirac. (At that time neither Dirac nor Harish-Chandra knew that V Bargmann in the USA and I M Gel'fand and M A Naimark in the USSR had already solved the problem.) He held forth enthusiastically about his solution and Dirac did not say a word. Then when Harish-Chandra stopped speaking, Dirac said softly that he would look at the written version. A week later, Dirac told Harish-Chandra to write up his work in the form of a paper. Harish-Chandra was disappointed that Dirac would not make any other comments on his work. Dirac seemed to be rather detached and not prone to excitement. It was a rare occasion when Dirac on his own offered his opinion on anyone's work. Sometimes, though, one could elicit some comments from him by explicit questions. T S Chang used to bemoan the fact that Dirac did not even read some of the papers he (Dirac) was communicating to journals. After Cambridge, Harish-Chandra wanted to go to the Institute for Advanced Study in Princeton and approached Dirac for a recommendation. Dirac declined on the ground that Bhabha, being more conversant with Harish-Chandra's work, was more qualified to do it. The Institute wrote to Harish-Chandra that Dirac would be at the Institute and was entitled to an assistant, and so he should ask Dirac whether he had any objection to Harish-Chandra being named as his assistant. Dirac had none, and Harish-Chandra went to Princeton in the summer of 1947 to work in pure mathematics.

Colloquia

The weekly colloquium in theoretical physics resumed in Lent term 1945, with A H Wilson in charge. Dirac gave three talks on his work and that of Bhabha and Harish-Chandra on the classical theory of point particles. During these talks Wilson asked about the work of M H L Pryce and of Harish-Chandra on the removal of infinite self-energies of point particles. Dirac replied that he did not particularly like that line of work. I followed Dirac and gave two talks on Mathisson's work. As soon as I started speaking, Wilson asked some questions. Before I could answer, Dirac had answered the questions for me. Dirac was trying to protect me. But when he saw that I could handle the questions he left it to me, except to make supportive comments now and then. At the end of the second talk, Wilson was speaking to me when Dirac joined us and Wilson said to Dirac, 'Dirac, you remember you did not understand some part of Mathisson's work', referring to Dirac's footnote in Mathisson's posthumous (1942) paper that he was omitting some work found in Mathisson's notes because he did not understand it. Dirac replied that it was not that he could not understand it but that it was wrong. Then Dirac said to me that Mrs Mathisson still had her late husband's notes and perhaps I should examine them. I kept quiet because, being a novice in research, I did not know whether I could cope with the task. So nothing happened. In the mean time Dirac did not want to speak too often at the colloquia and asked for a volunteer to report on his quantum electrodynamics. E H Sondheimer, who was Wilson's student, agreed to speak. After Sondheimer finished his talks, Wilson asked Dirac whether he would like to add anything. Dirac spoke for a few minutes, found that he had forgotten some of the details, and had to consult his papers to complete his remarks. In his remarks he emphasised that he did not believe his quantum electrodynamics was the right theory because it was so complicated and ugly. In Easter term 1945 Dirac reported on a paper by H W Peng (on divergence difficulty in quantum field theory and radiation reaction) which he was refereeing for the Royal Society. In the talk he mentioned that he could not understand some parts of the paper and that he had written directly to Peng for clarification. In Michaelmas term 1945 F Hoyle and M H L Pryce appeared at the colloquia. I remember Hoyle's talk on the abundances of the elements. Pryce did not like one of Hoyle's assumptions and just would not let Hoyle continue. When the situation was getting a little awkard, Dirac remarked that one could tentatively accept Hoyle's assumption and hear out Hoyle. And the talk proceeded. In Lent term 1946 Harish-Chandra spoke about his work on relativistic wave equations, which he had done before coming to Cambridge. He was using mathematics well above the heads of the audience. Dirac tried to make the talk intelligible by making Harish-Chandra deal with simpler cases rather than the general case he wanted to treat. During this term, statisticians like M S Bartlett, L S Goddard and J E Moyal were attending the colloquia. Once I overheard Moyal ask Dirac what he thought of a manuscript Moyal had sent to him. Dirac replied that he did not agree with Moyal. During this term Dirac again asked me to report on some work just completed, but I declined. In a talk by T S Chang in Easter term 1946, the question of the meaning of proper time in quantum mechanics arose. Dirac was quiet during the lively discussion that ensued. Then Chang directly asked Dirac for his opinion on the question. Dirac softly replied that, since one does not have a world line (trajectory) in quantum mechanics, one could not speak of proper time. The weekly colloquia took place regularly till the end of Easter term 1946. After that, I attended no more colloquia.

Random remembrances

Normally Dirac did not lecture in the Easter term. But towards the end of Lent term 1945 the students in his quantum mechanics class appealed to him to give them a further course of lectures during Easter term. Dirac wanted time to think about it. At the next lecture he announced that he would give a course of eight lectures on spinor analysis. Needless to say, it was a superb course. During this course he stated that he preferred B L van der Waerden's spinor form of the relativistic equations for the electron to his own matrix form.

During the Easter vacation 1945, H Samara and I thought that it would be a good idea to visit the Dublin Institute for Advanced Studies during the following long vacation. In reply to my enquiry, the Institute said that we could go and that Dirac would be there in July 1945 to participate in their Colloquium, but that we should ask Dirac to write to the Institute about us. When I showed the letter to Dirac, he was a little taken aback that I knew of his Dublin visit, but he readily agreed to write to Dublin even about Samara, whom he did not know at all. (When we were students, we never knew anything of Dirac's scientific activities outside Cambridge or even of his papers in course of publication unless he *had* to tell us.) The war was still on and so we had to apply to the UK Passport Office for permission to go to Dublin. Again Dirac readily agreed to write a letter to the Passport Office supporting our applications. When Miss Ashauer learnt of our plans, she also decided to go to Dublin. Dirac even told me which flight he would be taking from Liverpool to Dublin so that we could take the same flight. At Dublin airport Dirac was met by W Heitler and other people from the Institute. At some stage he brought them to us and made sure that they would look after us during our stay in Dublin. We were all very touched by Dirac's kindness and thoughtfulness.

At his first lecture on quantum mechanics in Michaelmas term 1945, Dirac entered the room to find it jammed with students. He obviously did not expect to see so many students at his lecture because he announced, 'This is a lecture on quantum mechanics.' No one moved. He repeated the announcement. Nothing happened again. The great upsurge in student interest in his lectures might have been due to the fact that the news reports of the atomic bomb in August 1945 featured Dirac as one of the participants in the British effort.

In Cambridge I knew one D V A S Amarasekara. He had to give up his studies just before completing Part III of the Mathematical Tripos because of a nervous breakdown. But he was also an artist and he began to paint again when he felt better. (DVASA was the way he signed his paintings.) He painted the portraits of many Cambridge luminaries. While Dirac was sitting for his portrait, DVASA tried to engage him in conversation on a variety of subjects. But when it came to anything outside physics and mathematics, Dirac told him that he had no interest or opinions whatever, especially in metaphysics, philosophy, religion and such subjects. Walter M Elsasser says something similar in his *Memoirs of a Physicist in the Atomic Age*.[2] One day Mrs Dirac was saying how their two young daughters were attached to DVASA during the painting sessions. Then Dirac wanted to know where DVASA was and what he was doing.

In Easter term 1951 I happened to see an item in the *Cambridge Daily News* that the University of Torino in Italy had conferred an honorary degree on Dirac. The next day, at the colloquium, I asked him whether he had been in Italy the previous day. He replied that he had not been and added that he did not believe in honorary degrees. During his sabbatical year 1954–5, Dirac could not go to the USA because of visa difficulties. So he agreed to spend part of the time at the Tata Institute of Fundamental Research in Bombay, India, and the other part at the National Research Council in Ottawa, Canada. (On the sea voyage from Bombay to Japan on his way to Canada, he became seriously ill with hepatitis, which disrupted his plans in Canada.) G Herzberg thought it would be a good gesture for a local university to confer honorary degrees on Dirac and J R Oppenheimer during the Colloquium organised in Ottawa to honour Dirac. He asked me whether Dirac would accept.

I recounted the conversation in 1951 and suggested that he could sound out Dirac nevertheless. Dirac declined straight away, and so the whole idea was abandoned.

In a conversation in Ottawa about people being shy, Dirac was quick to point out that he was shy too.

In January 1956, after Lamb and Kusch had received the Nobel Prize for their experimental work, I remarked to Dirac that perhaps it was time now for the theoreticians (like Feynman, Schwinger and Tomonaga) to receive their Nobel award. Dirac replied that he did not think that they would get a Nobel Prize because it was difficult for theoretical work to get that recognition unless that work helped experimentalists. On the same subject, the *New York Times* reported just a few years ago that Dirac had never nominated anyone for the Nobel Prize.

At every turn Dirac spoke (privately and publicly) of his profound dissatisfaction with the renormalisation method in quantum field theory: to him it was a stop-gap. What disturbed him most was that other eminent physicists did not feel the need to seek new and perhaps radical ways to overcome the infinities. For example, on a visit to Cornell University he had discussed the matter with H A Bethe, and the next day in Ottawa he expressed his unhappiness that Bethe was quite content with renormalisation.

One almost never sees any reference to a supreme example of Dirac's foresight. In the 1940s, whenever the occasion arose, Dirac used to argue forcefully against the requirement of space-reflection invariance and of time-reflection invariance for physical theories. Such a discussion took place in early 1946 with Harish-Chandra in the context of relativistic wave equations. These then-heretical ideas had such a shattering impact on Harish-Chandra that he rushed over to tell me about them. Dirac recorded his prophetic thoughts in 1949.[3] In 1959, in introducing Dirac to an audience at the National Research Council in Ottawa, G Herzberg quoted this prophetic paragraph of Dirac's. After the lecture, Dirac told me that he had forgotten that he had actually published his thoughts. On his return to Princeton, Dirac seems to have shown this paragraph to A Pais. In the early 1960s Pais mentioned this in an article dedicated to some physicist (living or dead). Unfortunately I am unable to locate the article now†.

---

† In his new book[4] Pais quotes and updates his earlier account of this particular conversation with Dirac.

Notes and References

1 See *Properties of Fundamental Interactions* 1973 ed A Zichichi vol 9 pt C (Bologna: Editrice Compositori) p. 989
2 Elsasser W M 1978 *Memoirs of a Physicist in the Atomic Age* (New York: Science History Publications and Bristol: Adam Hilger) p. 51
3 Dirac P A M 1949 *Rev. Mod. Phys.* **21** 392–9 (see especially the paragraph below equation (1) on p. 393)
4 Pais A 1986 *Inward Bound* (Oxford: Clarendon) pp. 25, 26, 31

Some Reminiscences of Professor P A M Dirac

C J Eliezer

My supervision by Professor Dirac

It was by a chance circumstance that Professor Dirac agreed to supervise me for the PhD. He usually did not take on students. In June 1941, after completing Part III of the Tripos, I was intending to stay on for research, and Dr A H Wilson had agreed to supervise me. During that long vacation, however, Dr Wilson was called away on war work. In early October I had a letter from Professor Dirac, in his very neat handwriting, which went something like this: 'As I am appointed your supervisor, come up and see me sometime. I lecture Tuesdays, Thursday, Saturdays at 10, and the best time to catch me is after a lecture.'

I saw him at the earliest opportunity, and showed him some papers I had been reading about mesons, which were new particles then. Dirac looked at them carefully and said: 'These are interesting particles—our theories for all particles have some serious difficulties when we consider how they interact with each other. It is better to try to solve the difficulty for the simplest of all particles —the electron—before dealing with some complicated ones.' He said he had recently completed a theory of radiating electrons. He gave me a thick reprint and suggested that if I read it and found it of interest, we could then think of a specific problem.

My first paper

After months of my preliminary reading, Dirac suggested that I look into the hydrogen atom problem, with radiation taken into account. From the family of mathematical solutions, one had to select a physically acceptable solution.

I first tried the three-dimensional case, then the two-dimensional and finally the straight line case where an electron is projected towards a stationary proton. I had expected (and so had Dirac) that one would get different solutions with the electron hitting the proton in different ways. The differential equation concerned was the highly non-linear one

$$\sqrt{y^2 - 1}\, \frac{\mathrm{d}^2 y}{\mathrm{d}x^2} + \frac{\mathrm{d}y}{\mathrm{d}x} + \frac{3}{2x^2} = 0$$

where $y = \sqrt{(1 + u^2)}$ and $u = \mathrm{d}x/\mathrm{d}s$ the velocity. One had to ascertain the behaviour of y as x tends to zero.

Methods of solving non-linear differential equations were not well known in those days. I was foolish enough to think that an exact solution could exist, but I could not find one. I wrote off to Miss M L Cartwright and Professor J E Littlewood for advice. Both of them very kindly helped. It turned out that the electron got stopped before it could reach the proton.

I told this to Dirac, and he seemed surprised. Then he asked the obvious question which foolishly I had not asked myself. What does the electron do after it gets stopped? At the spur of the moment, I said: 'The electron would start moving outwards, then come to a halt, and move back towards the proton and get stopped, probably closer to the proton, and continue this oscillating motion till it falls into the proton.' Dirac's face lit up with pleasure. That is a very beautiful solution, he said.

I left the room in high spirits. But my elation was short lived. When I worked out the equation, I found that the electron, after its first stop, would move away from the proton in a run-away type solution. At the earliest opportunity, I met Dirac again and told him. He said he too had worked it out and come to the same conclusion. Write up what you have in a paper, he said. That paper was published in the *Proceedings of the Cambridge Philosophical Society* (1943).

Other reminiscences

Whittaker was giving some lecture series at Cambridge on Eddington's work. I told Dirac that I had been attending. He said he had been intending to do so, but had not made it. I sketched the argument for 137 as the value of the fine-structure constant $\hbar c/e^2$. Dirac said: 'He first proved for 136, and when experiment raised to 137, he gave a proof for that.' He sounded sceptical.

I spoke to Dirac about E A Milne. He said that he found the idea of varying cosmical constants interesting but that he did not think there was much mathematics behind Milne's work.

I asked Dirac about Kaluza's work—on particle field equations in five dimensions. He said that it was interesting mathematically but unlikely to produce any different physics.

I asked Dirac what he considered to be his most important work. He said that it was the wave equation of the electron. If he had not done it at the time he did, Kramers would have—Kramers was rather close to it, he said.

I have a great many memories—not only of a brilliant mind who was so utterly dedicated to understanding our universe, but also of a human spirit that was ever helpful, kind and so very good.

Part II

Dirac's Contributions to Physics and Mathematics

Dirac's Contribution to the Early Development of Quantum Mechanics

Jagdish Mehra

In June 1968, at the Trieste Symposium on Contemporary Physics —organised by Professor Abdus Salam—Paul Dirac introduced Werner Heisenberg when he gave one of the evening lectures in the series 'From a life of physics'. Dirac said: 'I have the best of reasons for admiring Heisenberg. He and I were young research students at the same time, about the same age, working on the same problem. Heisenberg succeeded where I failed. There was a large mass of spectroscopic data accumulated at that time and Heisenberg found the proper way of handling it. In doing so he started the golden age of theoretical physics, and for a few years after that it was easy for any second-rate student to do first-rate work.'

As it turned out, Dirac was himself one of the principal architects of the golden age of theoretical physics. There is much that would be interesting to talk about in Paul Adrien Maurice Dirac's growing up and education in Bristol, his arrival in Cambridge in 1923, his work as a student here, and his brief apprenticeship in research with R H Fowler before very soon becoming a fully fledged quantum physicist in his own right. However, in view of time available to me I shall talk about the subject assigned to me, which is 'Dirac's Contribution to the Early Development of Quantum Mechanics'.

Werner Heisenberg was the first person to propose a scheme of quantum-theoretical kinematics and dynamics in a paper which he completed at Helgoland on 9 July 1925 and gave to Max Born in the middle of July. In it he had obtained the quantum condition, that was equivalent to the sum rule of Kuhn and Thomas, as

$$h = 4\pi m \sum_{\alpha=0}^{\infty} \{\,|\,a(n,\,n+\alpha)\,|^2 \omega(n+\alpha,\,\alpha)$$

$$- |\,a(n,\,n-\alpha)\,|^2\, \omega(n,\,n-\alpha)\} \qquad (1)$$

where the quantities within the brackets are related to the transition amplitudes and the frequencies. [1]

When Born read Heisenberg's paper, he was, as he has said, just 'fascinated'. Born put Heisenberg's quantum condition in the matrix notation as,

$$\sum_k [\,p(nk)q(kn) - q(nk)p(kn)\,] = \frac{h}{2\pi \mathrm{i}} \qquad (2)$$

and determined that the two matrix elements pq and qp were not identical. Born guessed that the non-diagonal elements of the matrix $pq - qp$ were zero, and the quantum condition could be written in general as,

$$pq - qp = \frac{h}{2\pi \mathrm{i}}\, 1 \qquad (3)$$

where 1 on the right-hand side is a unit matrix. Born invited Pauli to collaborate with him in developing matrix mechanics, but Pauli gave a sarcastic refusal. Born immediately persuaded Jordan to help him in his work, which led to Born and Jordan's matrix formulation of quantum mechanics, being completed on 27 September 1925. [2]

Further development towards the completion of the matrix scheme of quantum mechanics began immediately afterwards in collaboration of Born, Heisenberg and Jordan. Born, Heisenberg and Jordan's paper was thus the third paper after Heisenberg's discovery, and it gave a logically consistent exposition of matrix mechanics. It was completed by the end of October 1925, and is usually called the *'Drei-Männer Arbeit'* or 'Three-Man Paper'. [3]

Just before Born, Heisenberg and Jordan's paper was published in the *Zeitschrift für Physik* in January 1926, another paper, containing the complete scheme of quantum mechanics made its appearance in the *Proceedings of the Royal Society*. [4]

Let us go back to the moment in July 1925 when Heisenberg gave his paper on quantum-theoretical kinematics to Max Born.

Immediately after depositing the paper with Born, Heisenberg left for Leiden and Cambridge. In Cambridge, he stayed with R H Fowler, with whom he had become acquainted in Copenhagen. On 28 July 1925, Heisenberg addressed the Kapitza Club, which had been founded by Peter Kapitza for the discussion of research problems of modern physics. The subject of his talk was 'Term Zoology and Zeeman Botany', dealing with the enormous difficulties of masterminding the details of atomic spectroscopy with the help of *ad hoc* rules. It is remarkable that Heisenberg chose to speak on this subject, even though he seems to have found the solution of the quantum riddle quite recently. He was apparently not certain that the solution was really in hand. However, he did talk to Fowler about his new scheme.

Paul Dirac, then a research student of Fowler's in Cambridge, probably attended Heisenberg's seminar, and he himself gave a talk at the Kapitza Club one week later. Fowler received the proof sheets of Heisenberg's paper at the beginning of September 1925, found it interesting, but was a bit uncertain about it and wanted to know what Dirac's reaction would be. Dirac has said: 'I was so impressed then with the Hamiltonian formalism as the basis of atomic physics, that I thought anything not connected with it would not be much good. I thought there was not much in it [i.e. in Heisenberg's paper] and I put it aside for a week or so.'

When Dirac went back to it, it suddenly became clear to him that Heisenberg's idea had provided the key to the 'whole mystery'. During the following weeks Dirac tried to connect Heisenberg's quantum-theoretical re-interpretation of kinematical quantities with the action-angle variables of the Hamilton—Jacobi theory. 'I worked on it intensively from September 1925', Dirac said. 'During a long walk on a Sunday it occurred to me that the commutator might be the analogue of the Poisson bracket, but I did not know very well then what a Poisson bracket was. I had just read a bit about it, and forgotten most of what I had read. I wanted to check up on this idea, but I could not do so because I did not have any book at home which gave Poisson brackets, and all the libraries were closed. So I had to wait impatiently until Monday morning when the libraries were open and check on what Poisson bracket really was. Then I found that they would fit, but I had one impatient night of waiting.'

From the very beginning Dirac's clarification of the relationship between Heisenberg's variables and the classical variables made the formulation look more classical, and at the same time it very clearly isolated the small point at which the reformulation had to make a break with the classical theory.

From the quantum conditions expressed in angular variables Dirac found the correspondence between Heisenberg's commutation brackets and the classical Poisson brackets for the variables X and Y,

$$XY - YX = -\hbar\left\{\frac{\partial X}{\partial q_r}\frac{\partial Y}{\partial p_r} - \frac{\partial Y}{\partial q_r}\frac{\partial X}{\partial p_r}\right\} \tag{4}$$

where the q_r and p_r can be regarded as the action-angle variables w_r and J_r.

Dirac was now safely back on Hamiltonian ground. He showed his new results to Fowler who fully appreciated their importance. Fowler knew what was going on in Copenhagen and Göttingen, and he realised that there would be competition from these places. He thought that the results obtained in England in this field had to be published at once, and urged the *Proceedings of the Royal Society* to give immediate priority to the publication of Dirac's paper on 'The Fundamental Equations of Quantum Mechanics'. Sir James Jeans, who was then editor of the *Proceedings* and Secretary of the Royal Society, was ready and willing to oblige. All of Dirac's papers from 1925 to 1933 were thus published very rapidly.

In his fundamental paper, Dirac first gave a summary of Heisenberg's ideas, simplifying the mathematics and making it at once more elegant. He anticipated all the essential results of the papers of Born and Jordan and Born, Heisenberg and Jordan. He developed a quantum algebra, derived Heisenberg's quantisation rules, and obtained the canonical equations of motion for quantum systems. In the same paper, Dirac introduced an early form of creation and annihilation operators.

Dirac quickly followed this paper by another a few weeks later. In it he developed the algebra of q-numbers, that is, the dynamical variables which satisfy all the rules of normal numbers except their product is not necessarily commutative. He gave detailed theorems on the operations with q-numbers, and applied the rules he had obtained to multiply periodic systems in close analogy with the old quantum rules.[5]

Dirac's aim was to apply his scheme to the hydrogen atom. He wrote its Hamiltonian by simply replacing position and momentum variables in the classical Hamiltonian by q-numbers, and proceeded to obtain the Balmer formula in order to show that this abstract scheme could give results closely related to experiments. Dirac, however, did not go into the details of this calculation as Pauli (in his paper published during the same month, March 1926) had already shown that this could be done, and Dirac mentioned it in a footnote. He then went on to calculate the various features of the splitting and intensities of spectral lines in a magnetic field (including the Zeeman effect) in agreement with the experiments.

With all this work on the principles of quantum mechanics Dirac was awarded the PhD degree in May 1926 at Cambridge.

Erwin Schrödinger's paper on 'Quantization as an eigenvalue problem', the first of a series of papers that followed in quick succession establishing the framework of wave mechanics, was received by the editor of *Annalen der Physik* on 27 January 1926.[6] Schrödinger had constructed a theory which, at first sight, seemed to be quite different from the schemes developed in Göttingen and Cambridge. Based on the ideas of de Broglie, his theory employed a wavefunction for which he wrote down a linear equation, imposing certain boundary conditions. Schrödinger succeeded in reproducing the calculation for the spectrum of hydrogen in about three pages. Schrödinger himself gave a proof that Heisenberg's matrix equations could be replaced by his differential equations, showing the equivalence of the two schemes with respect to the results they yielded.[7]

Since Dirac had developed a 'good scheme' of his own and was pursuing its consequences, he was 'delayed' in reading Schrödinger's first article. When he finally did study it, he was a trifle annoyed because now he had to learn about another method which obviously also worked well. In contrast to the people at Göttingen, however, whose first reaction was that Schrödinger's wavefunction could not have any real physical meaning, Dirac had no 'philosophical' prejudice against it.

As was customary with him, Dirac first recast Schrödinger's theory in his own formalism. He noted the fact that, just as one might consider p and q as dynamical variables, one should also consider the negative energy $-E$ and the time as variables corresponding to the differential equations,

$$p_r = -i\hbar \frac{\partial}{\partial q_r} \quad \text{and} \quad -E = -i\hbar \frac{\partial}{\partial t}. \quad (5)$$

He had already introduced this step a few months earlier in a paper on 'Relativity quantum mechanics with an application to Compton scattering', where he talked about 'quantum time' with a view to introducing relativity into quantum mechanics.[8] From equation (5) he drew two conclusions: first, that only rational functions of E and p have meaning; second that one cannot multiply in general an equation containing p and E by a factor from the right-hand side. Dirac rewrote the Schrödinger equation in the form

$$F(q_r, p_r, t, E)\psi = [H(q, p, t) - E]\psi = 0 \quad (6)$$

remarking that Heisenberg's original quantum mechanics follows from a special choice of eigenfunctions.

In the same paper, Dirac proceeded to make another very important contribution by giving a general treatment of systems containing several identical particles.[9] Dirac said that if there is a system with, say, two electrons, and one considers two states (mn) or more accurately $(m(1), n(2))$ and $(m(2), n(1))$, which are distinguished only by the fact that in the second state two electrons have been interchanged, then according to his and Heisenberg's scheme, one has to count the two states as one. With this counting procedure, however, one cannot easily describe functions which are antisymmetrical in the electron coordinates. The general expression for the two-particle eigenfunction is

$$\psi_{mn} = a_{mn}\psi_m(1)\psi_n(2) + b_{mn}\psi_m(2)\psi_n(1). \quad (7)$$

There exist, however, only two choices for the coefficients a and b. Either

$$a_{mn} = b_{mn} \quad \text{symmetrical case (Bose–Einstein statistics)} \quad (8)$$

or

$$a_{mn} = -b_{mn} \quad \text{antisymmetrical case (Fermi–Dirac statistics).}$$

$$(9)$$

The latter case, equation (9) follows from Pauli's exclusion principle which holds for electrons. Dirac then went on to consider gases of free particles in volume V, obeying either Bose–Einstein statistics or the statistics deduced from the exclusion principle. From the number N_s of particles in the sth set (having the same energy E_s) he derived,

$$N_s = \frac{A_s}{\exp[(\alpha + E_s)/kT] + 1} \tag{10a}$$

where

$$A_s + 2V(2m)^{3/2}E_s^{1/2}\frac{\mathrm{d}E_s}{(2\pi\hbar)^3} \tag{10b}$$

and α is related to the density.

In his celebrated paper of February 1924 'On the "Anschaulichen" content of quantum-theoretical kinematics and dynamics', in which he introduced the uncertainty relations, Heisenberg proceeded on the basis of the transformation theory of Jordan and Dirac, indicating thereby that the transformation theory belonged to the most reliable foundations of quantum theory. [10]

The canonical transformations had already played an important role in the formulation of matrix and q-number mechanics. Dirac's main work on transformation theory was contained in his paper of autumn 1926 on 'The physical interpretation of quantum dynamics'. [11] Dirac's principal step was the introduction of the δ-function as a mathematical tool. The δ-function, which is supposed to be zero everywhere in its range of definition except at the point $x = 0$, helped to formulate matrices with continuous indices and their transformations. Dirac was able to derive Schrödinger's differential equation from quantum mechanics. By doing so, he closed the physical proof of the identity of all schemes in the new quantum theory. The impact of this paper, which Dirac submitted from Copenhagen in December 1926, was great. Besides introducing the δ-function, which posed many problems for the mathematicians, Dirac had created a powerful method similar to the canonical transformations of the old Hamiltonian theory. Dirac now felt, quite justifiably, that the new scheme could indeed replace classical dynamics.

Fowler had been quite keen that Dirac should go to Copenhagen for a year, but Dirac himself was worried about going to a country where he did not know the language. He actually preferred to visit Germany because he knew a little German. He made a compromise and decided to spend about half a year in Copenhagen and another half in Göttingen. In the autumn of 1926, Dirac left for Copenhagen, arriving there in the middle of September.

Life in Copenhagen, especially in Bohr's Institute, was different from what it had been in Cambridge. Dirac spent most of his time in Bohr's Institute, and he met new people there quite often. Copenhagen was different from Göttingen and Cambridge, where most of the work on quantum theory had actually been done. 'Without Bohr, I think, there would have been nothing', Dirac has remarked. 'I was very much impressed by hearing Bohr talk. It was just a very moving experience to be with Bohr.'

Dirac's paper on 'The quantum theory of the emission and absorption of radiation', communicated to the *Proceedings of the Royal Society* by Niels Bohr in early 1927, treated the problem of building a relativistic quantum theory.[12] But the difficulties involved were so great that Dirac found it worthwhile to look into an approximation which was not strictly relativistic. As the total system, he considered an atom in interaction with a radiation field. In order to have a discrete number of degrees of freedom for the radiation field, he enclosed the system in a finite box, and decomposed the radiation into its Fourier components. Now, expanding the wavefunction of the interacting system (i.e. of the radiation and the atom, the electric field of the atom being approximated by a varying dipole potential) into those of free radiation, he chose the following dynamical variables:

$$b_r = N_r^{1/2} \exp(-i\theta_r/\hbar) \qquad \text{and} \qquad b_r^\dagger = N_r^{1/2} \exp(+i\theta_r/\hbar). \quad (11)$$

The dagger here denotes the Hermitian conjugate, N_r is the absolute square of the Fourier coefficient a_r, and θ_r is a phase variable conjugate to N_r. For b he assumed the commutation relations,

$$b_r b_r^\dagger - b_r^\dagger b_r = 1. \quad (12)$$

Dirac recognised the nature of b and $b^\dagger$ as annihilation and creation operators, showing that the interaction of the atom with the radiation causes transitions of photons with energy E_r into those with energy E_s. By calculating the matrix elements for these transitions, Dirac obtained Einstein's A and B coefficients as functions of the interaction potential.

A year after this first paper on 'second quantisation', Jordan and Wigner developed a similar scheme for Fermi fields.

Soon after Christmas 1926 Dirac went from Copenhagen to Göttingen. On the way he stopped off in Hamburg to attend a meeting of the German Physical Society. In Hamburg he also met Pauli, whom he knew personally from Copenhagen. They got along pretty well, especially since Pauli was able to understand Dirac's point of view more quickly than most people, and Dirac had the impression that Pauli appreciated his scientific attitude even more than Heisenberg's. It is possible that he also met Sommerfeld in Hamburg at that time, or got to know him during his visit to Göttingen sometime later.

Dirac once told me: 'I remember once when I was in Copenhagen, that Bohr asked me what I was working on and I told him I was trying to get a satisfactory relativistic theory of the electron. And Bohr said: "But Klein and Gordon have already done that!" That answer first rather disturbed me; Bohr seemed quite satisfied by Klein's solution, but I was not because of the negative probabilities that it led to. I just kept on with it, worrying about getting a theory which would have only positive probabilities.'

In 1926 Klein had obtained a relativistic equation for a scalar field by inserting quantum operators for momentum and energy in the equation:

$$E^2 = p^2 c^2 + m_0^2 c^4. \tag{13}$$

The resulting equation was also independently discovered by Gordon in Hamburg, and by several other people including Schrödinger himself, and is now referred to as the Klein–Gordon equation;[13] it is

$$\Delta \psi - \frac{1}{c^2} \frac{\partial^2 \psi}{\partial t^2} - \left(\frac{m_0 c^2}{\hbar} \right)^2 = 0. \tag{14}$$

The difficulties which perturbed Dirac were connected with two questions. First, if one used the Klein–Gordon equation for a single particle and interpreted the expression

$$\psi^*(x) \frac{\partial \psi(x)}{\partial t} - \psi(x) \frac{\partial \psi^*(x)}{\partial t} = \rho(x) \tag{15}$$

as the probability of finding this particle at a certain place, then one could have a negative probability. Secondly, Dirac had already set up the transformation theory in its general form which was a very powerful tool, and he felt that it was not only correct, but had to be preserved and brought into harmony with relativity. For achieving this goal, he needed an equation linear in time.

Dirac started by 'playing with equations rather than trying to introduce the right physical idea'. By 'introducing the right physical idea' Dirac meant the idea of spin. The spin of the electron had already been introduced by Uhlenbeck and Goudsmit in 1925, to explain the doublet structure of the single-electron spectra without the hypothesis of 'non-mechanical stress'. Pauli had developed the theory of the spinning electron further and described the electron by a two-component wavefunction, which could be used for explaining the empirical spectral data using a non-relativistic Schrödinger equation.

Dirac's intention was to go beyond such an approximation. A scalar product in three dimensions could be formed from Pauli's σ-matrices and the momentum, and he wanted to extend it to four-dimensional space–time. After several weeks of concentrated effort he discovered the simple solution that he could do so by generalising the 2×2 σ-matrices to 4×4 matrices, which he called γ-matrices. From the generalisation of the σ-algebra, it naturally followed that the γ should anticommute. In his derivation of the equation, Dirac had set things up in the absence of a field. The homogeneity of space and time required that the coefficients of the momenta were independent of space and time, and he obtained the relativistic equation, [14]

$$\left(i \sum_{\mu=1}^{4} \gamma_\mu p_\mu + m \cdot c\right)\psi = 0 \tag{16}$$

where

$$\gamma_\mu^2 = 1 \qquad \gamma_\mu\gamma_\nu + \gamma_\nu\gamma_\mu = 2\delta_{\mu\nu}.$$

In the same paper, received by the editor on 2 January 1928, he then introduced an arbitrary electromagnetic field and replaced the components of the four-momentum by a relativistic extension of the equation,

$$p = m\dot{q} - \frac{e}{c} A \qquad [H = \text{curl } A]. \tag{17}$$

Finally he used his equation to describe the motion of electrons in a centrally symmetric field, giving a treatment of the hydrogen spectrum.

In his second contribution on 'The quantum theory of the electron', submitted a month after the first, Dirac proceeded to calculate the states of the hydrogen atom in his new theory. He inferred that the theory will give consistent results that are invariant under a Lorentz transformation. In a lecture in Leipzig in June 1928 he summarised the results. It followed from his theory that in the alkali spectra the electron had to have a spin of magnitude $\frac{1}{2}\hbar$.

In his Leipzig lecture he also mentioned the problem which had bothered him the most. If one writes the wave equation with $-e$ instead of e (the electron charge), one would expect something completely new, and he speculated that it might refer to the proton. The equation, however, did not give it. He concluded at the time that, if there were no transitions between $+e$ and $-e$ solutions of the wave equation, it was not too bad. In his theory the transition probability turned out to be finite, albeit very small, being of the fourth order in (v/c), where v is the velocity of the electron. The theory could therefore only be an approximation to nature; one probably had to change the concepts entirely, even bringing in asymmetry of the laws between past and future.

During the next two years Dirac did not publish anything on the relativistic equation. This was not only due to the fact that he was lecturing and preparing the first edition of his book, *The Principles of Quantum Mechanics*, published in 1930, in which he included topics such as many-electron systems and quantum statistical mechanics. He knew that his relativistic theory was still imperfect, and in a paper on 'A theory of electrons and protons', published in 1930, he explicitly gave the explanation.[15] The wave equation had, in addition to 'solutions for which the kinetic energy of the electron is positive, an equal number of unwarranted solutions with negative kinetic energy for the electron, which appear to have no physical meaning'. By examining the wavefunction of a negative energy solution in an electromagnetic field, Dirac found that it behaved like a particle with positive charge. But this connection would not solve the problem if one did not also have the fact that the electrons obey the exclusion principle. He could therefore assume that 'there are so many electrons in the world that the most stable states are occupied, or more accurately that *all states of negative energy are occupied except perhaps a few of small velocity'*. Dirac argued that the transition of electrons from states with positive energy to those with negative energy was highly suppressed, and only the unoccupied negative states, the 'holes', could be observed. He assumed that 'the holes in the distribution of negative energy electrons are the protons. When an electron of positive energy drops into a hole and fills it up, we have an electron and proton disappearing together with the emission of radiation.'

In a paper read before the British Association for the Advancement of Science at Bristol on 8 September 1930, Dirac summarised his results. Matter consists, he said, of 'electrons and protons', and the existence of the protons 'follows from the relativistic wave equation'. A difficulty with this interpretation remained: in his theory Dirac could calculate the transition probability for the annihilation process only under the 'approximation' that the masses of the electrons and protons were equal, and the resulting amplitude was several orders of magnitude higher than that suggested by empirical evidence on 'electron–proton annihilations'. In spite of this problem Dirac had faith in the essential correctness of his interpretation of the wave equation.

After Dirac's publication of the electron wave equation in 1928, many people took up its study. Dirac himself worried about the unequal masses of the positively and negatively charged particles which existed in nature. Dirac recalled: 'I felt right at the start that the negative energy electrons would have the same rest mass as the ordinary electrons . . . . I hoped that there was some lack of symmetry somewhere which would bring in the extra mass for the positively charged ones. I was hoping that in some way the Coulomb interaction might lead to such an extra mass, but I couldn't see how it could be brought about.' After Weyl's careful investigations Dirac gave up the idea that the positively charged hole was a proton.

Then, on 2 August 1932, there came along the discovery of positron by Carl Anderson. For Dirac it meant the satisfaction that his equation predicted the situation correctly, as he had hoped. His work had also provided the first example in the history of physics where the existence of a new particle was predicted on a purely theoretical basis. Dirac himself considered much more important the fact that in his equation the spin had been incorporated so naturally, just following from the symmetry properties exhibited by the equations. At the seventh Solvay Conference in Brussels in October 1933, Dirac summarised the 'Theory of the positron'.[16] In his Nobel lecture on 12 December 1933, Dirac had the occasion to return to this topic and predict the existence of 'negative' protons as well.

References

1   Heisenberg W 1925 *Z. Phys.* **33** 879–93
2   Born M and Jordan P 1925 *Z. Phys.* **34** 858–88
3   Born M, Heisenberg W and Jordan P 1926 *Z. Phys.* **35** 557–615
4   Dirac P A M 1925 *Proc. R. Soc.* A **109** 642–53
5   Dirac P A M 1926 *Proc. R. Soc.* A **110** 561–79
6   Schrödinger E 1926 *Ann. Phys., Lpz.* **79** 361–76
7   Schrödinger E 1926 *Ann. Phys., Lpz.* **79** 734–56
8   Dirac P A M 1926 *Proc. R. Soc.* A **111** 405–23
9   Dirac P A M 1926 *Proc. R. Soc.* A **112** 661–77
10 Heisenberg W 1927 *Z. Phys.* **43** 172–98
11 Dirac P A M 1927 *Proc. R. Soc.* A **113** 621–41
12 Dirac P A M 1927 *Proc. R. Soc.* A **114** 243–65
13 Klein O 1926 *Z. Phys.* **37** 895
14 Dirac P A M 1928 *Proc. R. Soc.* A **117** 610–24; A **118** 351–61
15 Dirac P A M 1930 *Proc. R. Soc.* A **126** 360–5
16 See Mehra J 1975 *The Solvay Conferences on Physics* (Dordrecht: Reidel)

Dirac and the Interpretation of Quantum Mechanics

J C Polkinghorne

A student in the late mediaeval University of Paris was permitted, if adverse circumstances required it, to dispose of all his books except that he was not allowed to sell his copy of the Bible or his copy of the *Summa Theologiae* of St Thomas Aquinas. When I left Cambridge to become a curate in Bristol I did not sell my physics books but I did leave most of them behind me. However, I knew that I had to take with me my copy of that *Summa* of quantum theory, Dirac's *The Principles of Quantum Mechanics*.[1] It is still with me and I turned to it to prepare this talk on Dirac's concern with the interpretation of quantum mechanics.

We can consider the subject at three levels: structure of the formalism; the problem of measurement; and philosophical problems.

Structure of the formalism

What is it which, in all its possible varied expressions, gives to quantum mechanics its novel character, completely distinct from the character of the classical physics that preceded it? Dirac gives a clear, authoritative and convincing answer to that question. It is the principle of the superposition of states.

Quantum theory mixes together what was classically immiscible. In his Cambridge lectures, which followed closely the pattern of his book, Dirac expressed himself with the utmost clarity but the minimum of gesture and rhetorical effect. However, he did permit himself a slight indulgence near the start of the course. He broke a piece of chalk in two and said that classically there was a state where a piece of chalk was 'here' (indicating one half) and classically a state where it was 'there' (indicating the other). If the chalk were now replaced by an electron then there would also be quantum mechanical states where the electron was described by a superposition of 'here' and 'there'. These were to be interpreted not as corresponding to the electron's being somewhere in the middle (which was another state altogether) but in a probabilistic way that the electron would, on investigating its position, sometimes be found 'here' and sometimes be found 'there'. Thus the superposition principle leads us straight to the fitful and unpicturable character of the quantum world which distinguishes it from the determinate and clear world of classical physics.

It is well known that some of the pioneers of quantum theory, such as Einstein, de Broglie and Schrödinger, came greatly to dislike this indeterminate character of the subject they had fathered. Dirac did not share their disquiet. In his book he admits one might regret the loss of determinacy but says that is 'offset by a great simplification, provided by the general *principle of the superposition of states*'.[2] There is a sense in which the whole of *The Principles of Quantum Mechanics* is an essay on this theme.

In its later editions the book expresses the principle in terms of the bra and ket vector space formalism invented by Dirac. In his lectures Dirac was scrupulous in not underlining his own formidable contributions to quantum theory. However, one did gain the impression from a slight smile that played around his features when he introduced bras and kets that this invention (and the small and harmless joke enshrined in the nomenclature) had given him great satisfaction. Compared to his deep understanding of the structure of quantum mechanics, the quantisation of the electromagnetic field and the relativistic equation of the electron, bras and kets might seem a small matter, but appropriate notation is an important aid to fluency and insight in theoretical physics and mathematics. One has only to think of the superiority of Leibniz's dy/dx notation in the calculus over the fluxion notation of Dirac's great predecessor in the Lucasian Chair, Sir Isaac Newton. Bras and kets have proved a fruitful choice and are now universally used in quantum mechanical thinking.

The superposition principle inexorably leads to quantum mechanical indeterminacy, which in turn leads to the problem of measurement in quantum theory. An electron can be in a superposition of the states 'here' and 'there' but when we address to it the experimental question 'Where are you?' it has to settle for a particular answer on a particular occasion. How does it then come about that on that specific occasion we find it (say) 'here'; that its wavepacket collapses from the combination of the two possibilities onto the single state actually realised in that act of measurement? This is the second level at which we can discuss the interpretation of quantum mechanics.

The problem of measurement
We do not live in the quantum world but receive our experience in the apparently classical world of the every-day. An act of measurement involves a chain of correlated consequence by which a signal carrying information from the microscopic quantum world is amplified to become an observable result in the macroscopic every-day world. How do these worlds, the one cloudy and fitful, the other clear and reliable, interlock to provide a specific answer on a specific occasion?[3]

Consider the familiar Stern–Gerlach experiment to measure the spin of a proton. An unpolarised beam of protons is passed through an inhomogeneous magnetic field. If the proton's spin is 'up' then it is deviated in a particular direction and then its passage will make a particular Geiger counter click, which will then be heard by an observer. On the other hand, if the proton's spin is 'down' then it is deviated in the opposite direction and then a different Geiger counter will click which will then be heard by the observer. All that such an account gives us is a chain of correlations (if ... then ... then ...). The buck of decision seems just to be passed down the chain without it being clear at what point it actually becomes fixed that the proton's spin is 'up' on this particular occasion. The problem of quantum mechanical measurement is where does it become settled on a specific occasion that we get a specific result?

Three types of proposal have been made.

(i) The first proposal says that it occurs when the systems involved in the links of the chain are sufficiently 'large' to be considered as classical measuring apparatus. This is essentially the point of view of the Copenhagen interpretation hammered out by Niels Bohr and his friends and subsequently prescribed as an orthodoxy for the faithful. While I incline to think that this is the right track to be on, it also seems to me that Bohr never recognised that the way this works is problematic to an unresolved degree.

What is involved in this invocation of large systems is totally different from the well understood fact that they will behave in a way that is accurately approximated by classical mechanics. That insight simply says that each link in the chain becomes progressively tighter as the systems becomes larger; the correlations are more exact. It does not explain how the intervention of such large systems chooses *between* different chains of correlations, as is needed if a definite result is to be obtained.

The Copenhagen approach essentially divides up the physical world into two, the indeterminate quantum world and the determinate world of classical measuring apparatus. It is far from clear that such a juxtaposition can be made with consistency. After all there is in fact only one world; the measuring instruments are themselves composed of quantum mechanical constituents. In his long battle with Einstein about the uncertainty principle[4] Bohr had repeatedly to appeal to the fact that quantum mechanics must be whole-heartedly applied to all aspects of the physical investigation. Otherwise contradictions could indeed be obtained. Thus the supposed objectifying role of classical measuring apparatus is decidedly problematic.

(ii) The second proposal suggests that it is at the moment of the intervention of the consciousness of an observer that the result is finally determined. Here, at the interface of matter and mind, is surely a link in the chain of correlation of a manifestly novel character. May it not, then, be also the moment of decision? At first sight the proposal has a certain attraction but on reflection difficulties are apparent. It makes quantum mechanics an anthropocentric, or at best biocentric, phenomenon. Are we to suppose that in those parts of the universe and those times in its evolution when conscious beings have not been present, no unstable atom has for sure decayed? That print-out recording the results of a computerised quantum experiment, stored away in a drawer unread, only acquires a definite imprint months later when the drawer is opened and someone reads it? It takes a bit of swallowing.

(iii) Even more bizarre is the third proposal. This is the many-worlds interpretation of quantum mechanics. It asserts that at the moment of each act of quantum measurement the universe splits up into a series of 'parallel' disjoint universes in each of which one of the possible results of the measurement is realised. Since acts of quantum measurement are taking place all the time this is a proposal of astounding prodigality. We are continually being cloned as the world repeatedly divides. Popular as this notion has been with the 'gee-whizz' school of expositors of science for the general public it has not gained the approval of many professional physicists.

It is a central paradox of quantum mechanics that this highly successful predictive theory is still the subject of unresolved dispute about its interpretation. What does Dirac have to say to help us? The frank answer is tantalisingly little. Early in his book he writes

> Causality only applies when a system is left undisturbed. If a system is small we cannot observe it without producing a serious disturbance and hence [*sic*] we cannot expect to find any causal connections between the results of our observations.[5]

Later, when he discusses the collapse of the wavepacket (a phrase he does not use) he says

> When we measure a real dynamical variable ξ the disturbance involved in the act of measurement causes a jump in the state of the dynamical system ... measurement always causes the system to jump into an eigenstate of the variable that is measured.[6]

This unanalysed concept of 'disturbance' is presented as a cutting of the Gordian knot of the measurement process. I do not find this helpful or illuminating. The truth seems to be that Dirac was not very interested in the problem of measurement. The word does not appear in the rather exiguous index to *The Principles of Quantum Mechanics*.

Philosophical problems

Quantum mechanics raises critical ontological problems about what actually *is*. It profoundly modifies our view of the nature of the physical world.

In every-day life we may feel a good deal of sympathy for Dr Johnson when he kicked the stone and asserted that thereby he had refuted Bishop Berkeley. However, we now know that the solid-seeming stone is nearly all empty space and what is not is a weaving of wave-mechanical patterns. Heisenberg's uncertainty principle tells us that if we know where an electron is we do not know what it is doing and if we know what it is doing we do not know where it is. What reality can be attributed to the unpicturable and elusive quantum world?

Many of the founding fathers of quantum mechanics inclined to a positivistic view of the subject. That is to say they regarded it as a (highly successful) manner of speaking but did not attribute a full reality to the electrons and other denizens of the quantum world. The aim of physics was simply the harmonious interrelationship of experimental results. Thus Niels Bohr once said 'There is no quantum world. There is only abstract quantum physical description.'[7] I personally feel sure that this is incorrect. The remarkable and elegant structure of the microworld revealed to the investigations of modern elementary particle physics demands to be taken more seriously than that. Are we to believe that when Rubbia and his collaborators rightly got so excited about the discoveries of the W and Z particles at CERN in 1983 they were simply rejoicing at the harmonious reconciliation of the behaviour of a large and expensive array of electronic counters? I think not. They surely believed that they had added to our knowledge of what is.

Dirac in a formal way echoes the positivistic stance of his contemporaries. He writes

> only questions about the results of experiments have a real significance and it is only such questions that theoretical physics has to consider.[8]

Really? Why then did Dirac persistently refuse to accept renormalised quantum electrodynamics as a satisfactory physical theory? As an account of experimental data it is highly successful, giving values for the Lamb shift and the anomalous magnetic moment of the electron which agree with measurement to the available accuracy of a few parts per million. Dirac's scepticism about the theory was concerned with what he considered its unacceptably inelegant treatment of infinities and not with any reservation about its relation to experiment. He once wrote

> It is more important to have beauty in one's equations than to have them fit experiment ... because the discrepancy may be due to minor features which are not properly taken into account and that will get cleared up with further developments of the theory ... It seems that if one is working from the point of view of getting beauty in one's

equations and if one has a really sound instinct, one is on a sure line of progress.[9]

Those words are scarcely the words of a positivist, though they are the authentic words of a theoretical physicist—one moreover who in all his work displayed to the highest degree 'a really sound instinct'.

Dirac wrote in his book about the loss of picturability involved in quantum theory

> One may, however, extend the meaning of the word 'picture' to include any way of looking at the fundamental laws which makes their self-consistency obvious.[10]

That is at least half-way to acknowledging that understanding (or insight, as the Jesuit philosopher Bernard Lonergan would say) is the goal of theoretical physics. In my view it is physics' achievement of understanding of the quantum world which forms the basis for the defence of that world's reality, a reality which is more subtle than naive objectivity.

Let me finish where I began, with *The Principles of Quantum Mechanics,* a very great book written by a very great man, first published in 1930 and still an essential item in every quantum physicist's library. It does not answer every question about the interpretation of quantum mechanics—in our present state of knowledge no book can—but it conveys in a matchless way the elegance and excitement of the fundamental subject that its author did so much to found.

Notes and References

1   Dirac P A M *The Principles of Quantum Mechanics* (PQM) 4th edn 1958 (Oxford: Clarendon)
2   PQM p. 11
3   For a fuller discussion of the issues see Polkinghorne J C 1984 *The Quantum World* (London: Longman) Ch. 6
4   See Bohr N 1958 *Atomic Physics and Human Knowledge* (New York: Wiley) pp. 32–66

5 PQM p. 4
6 PQM p. 36
7 Quoted by Petersen A 1963 *Bull. Atom. Sci.* **19** 8–14
8 PQM p. 5
9 Dirac P A M 1963 *Sci. Am.* (May)
10 PQM p. 10

Dirac and Finite Field Theories

Abdus Salam

Introduction

Paul Adrien Maurice Dirac was undoubtedly one of the greatest physicists of this or any century. In three decisive years—1925, 1926 and 1927—with three papers, he laid the foundations, first of quantum physics, second of the quantum theory of fields, and third, of the theory of elementary particles with his famous equation of the electron. No man except Einstein has had such a decisive influence in so short a time on the course of physics in this century. For me personally, Dirac represented the highest reaches of personal integrity of anyone I have ever known. Thus, on this Commemorative Day, with sadness for his passing, and with deeply felt sympathy for his bereaved family, let me begin with sentiments of rejoicing for his life, and for our good fortune in having known him.

In speaking of Dirac's work today, I wish to take as my subject the area of renormalisation. Even though Dirac and Kramers were the first to emphasise the physical necessity of the concept of (finite) renormalisation (of the electron's mass) Dirac never approved of our use of this beautiful idea of renormalisation to hide away the infinities which appear in perturbation calculations in quantum electrodynamics. He believed that a finite field theory would eventually be discovered for all processes.

My generation of theoretical physicists was brought up on the work of Tomonaga, Schwinger and Feynman, and, in particular, of Dyson. Dyson proved that all infinities in quantum electrodynamics in each perturbative order could be absorbed into a renormalisation of electron mass and charge. This was an important result. Thus, at the price of not being able to compute these two quantities†, all scattering processes in quantum electro-dynamics could be made finite. This, in Dyson's view, was a small price to pay for a resolution of the field theoretic infinity problem. My generation avidly bought this idea, but not so Dirac.

Whilst recognising that such absorption of infinities through a renormalisation of mass and charge could be a temporary expedient, Dirac always insisted that there is no place for infinities in a fundamental field theory. He felt strongly that one should keep searching for a basic amelioration of the infinity problem.

It now appears that there is indeed a class of field theories which are perturbatively finite to all orders. If renormalisations of coupling constants and masses are physically necessary, these would only be finite renormalisations. The hitherto discovered field theories of this variety are non-Abelian gauge theories of the extended super-symmetric type. Whether such theories are physically relevant is not yet known, but they are mathematically elegant, and without doubt satisfy the criterion of beauty which Dirac always advocated.

Even more important, there has recently been developed a local field theory of extended‡ one-dimensional objects (strings). There is the promise—brought to a near proof—that closed-string super-symmetric field theories, whose long-range excitations must contain quantum gravity (as well as Yang–Mills excitations describing electro-nuclear interactions) may give rise to finite matrix elements. If this conjecture is finally proved, and if these theories prove to be physically relevant, Dirac would be fully vindicated.

Finite supersymmetric field theories
The finite supersymmetric field theories at present known fall into two classes.

(i) $N = 2$ Yang–Mills supersymmetric theories, where the Yang–Mills gauge particles (plus four-component gauginos and complex scalars) belong to the adjoint representation of the gauge group, e.g. SU(n). This Yang–Mills $N = 2$ supersymmetric multiplet interacts with $2n$ fundamental representation of $N = 2$

---

†There is a third infinity associated with the wavefunction of the electron, but this is gauge dependent and one can find gauges in which this quantity could be rendered finite.
‡Dirac, one may recall, was one of the pioneers of field theories of (two-dimensional) extended objects.

matter multiplets. There is no coupling of matter multiplets among themselves.

(ii) The second type of finite theories are the $N = 4$ Yang–Mills superymmetric field theories.

Let me describe the $N = 4$ Yang–Mills theories first. These are theories with an internal symmetry group SU(n). (The symmetry group could be any non-Abelian group G, but SU(n) is a good example.) This theory contains $(n^2 - 1)$ Yang–Mills spin-1 objects in the adjoint representation of SU(n), $4(n^2 - 1)$ two-component chiral fermions ψ_α and $3(n^2 - 1)$ complex scalar particles $H_{[\alpha\beta]}$, where $H_{41} = H^{32}$, etc with the index $\alpha = 1, 2, 3, 4$ characterising the underlying $N = 4$ supersymmetry.

The interaction Lagrangian is given by

$$\int d^4x \left[-\tfrac{1}{4} F_{\mu\nu}^2 - \bar{\psi}^\alpha i\!\!\not{\nabla}\psi_\alpha + \tfrac{1}{4} \nabla^\mu \bar{H}^{\alpha\beta} \cdot \nabla_\mu H_{\alpha\beta} \right.$$

$$\left. - \frac{g}{\sqrt{2}} (\bar{H}^{\alpha\beta} \cdot \psi_\alpha^T \times C^{-1}\psi_\beta + \text{h.c.}) \right. \tag{1}$$

$$\left. - \tfrac{1}{2} \sum_\alpha M_\alpha(a)(\psi_\alpha^T \cdot C^{-1}\psi_\alpha + \text{h.c.}) - V(H) \right]$$

where $V(H)$ is

$$V(H) = M^2(H_{14})|H_{14}|^2 + M^2(H_{24})|H_{24}|^2 + M^2(H_{34})|H_{34}|^2$$

$$- \frac{\sqrt{2}}{6} g \sum_\alpha M_\alpha(a)\varepsilon^{\alpha\beta\gamma\delta} H_{\beta\alpha} \cdot H_{\gamma\alpha} \times H_{\delta\alpha} + \text{h.c.} \tag{2}$$

$$+ \tfrac{1}{16} g^2 \bar{H}^{\alpha\beta} \times H^{\gamma\delta} \cdot H_{\alpha\beta} \times H_{\gamma\delta}.$$

The Lagrangian contains seven masses (four for the fermions ψ_α and three for the complex scalars H_{14}, H_{24}, H_{34}). The inclusion of these masses breaks supersymmetry softly. It can be shown that the Green functions of the theory exhibit no ultraviolet infinities, provided the following conditions are satisfied.

(i) The masses of the particles concerned obey the relation

$$M^2(H_{14}) + M^2(H_{24}) + M^2(H_{34}) =$$
$$M^2(\psi_1) + M^2(\psi_2) + M^2(\psi_3) + M^2(\psi_4).$$

(ii) The Green functions must be computed in the light cone gauge. If a general gauge is employed there will, of course, be no ultraviolet infinities on shell, but such infinities may arise for the off-shell wavefunction renormalisations.

(iii) If we restrict n to $n = 2$ (i.e. the internal gauge symmetry group is SU(2)) there are no infrared infinities in the theory either, i.e. the theory is completely finite in the light cone gauge, both for ultraviolet and infrared infinities.

(iv) For $n > 2$ some infrared infinities may remain associated with the SU$(n - 2)$ unbroken Yang–Mills symmetries due to the masslessness of the Yang–Mills vector particles, associated with the SU$(n - 2)$.

This result[1] is the most powerful to date of a series of results which started with the advent of supersymmetry in the latter part of 1973. I shall trace some of the steps in this development.

(i) For supersymmetric theories (with the same number of fermion and boson modes), Wess and Zumino showed that there was a mutual cancellation of loop infinities between fermions and bosons, such that the vertex-part infinities cancelled in a Yukawa type of supersymmetry theory. The only uncancelled infinities in such theories were those associated with the mass and the wavefunction renormalisations!

(ii) For Yang–Mills supersymmetric theories, however, the wavefunction renormalisations are infinite, and so are the vertex renormalisations. This implies a charge renormalisation. In an axial gauge, this renormalisation is associated with the wavefunction renormalisation of the gauge particles, i.e. $e_R = Z_3^{\frac{1}{2}} e$.

(iii) For $N = 4$ Yang–Mills theory without mass, it was noted by Avdeev et al,[2] Grisaru et al[3] and Caswell and Zanon[4] that up to three loops the β-function (which is a gauge-invariant quantity and which determines whether there is an infinity associated with charge renormalisation) is actually zero (i.e. $Z_3 = 1$ in $e_R = Z_3^{\frac{1}{2}} e$).

(iv) Suggestive arguments were given to all orders for the vanishing of the β-function by Ferrara and Zumino,[5] Sohnius and West[6] and Stelle.[7]

(v) These arguments were made quantitative and extended to include Green functions to all orders for the massless theory by Mandelstam[8] and Brink et al[9] in the light cone gauge. Not only was the gauge-invariant charge renormalisation finite, but in this gauge all the Zs were also finite.

(vi) There was, however, a worry that the massless fully supersymmetric theory may, after all, be a free field theory. One needed to see if the results on finiteness would survive the breaking of supersymmetry implied by the addition of mass terms. Such additions of mass terms are expected to be gentle, so far as the infinities are concerned. This led to the investigation by Namazie *et al* mentioned above.[1] We discovered that if the supertrace of M^2 is equal to zero, and a specific set of cubic terms of the type indicated in (i) and (ii) are added to the Lagrangian (together with the mass terms), the theory retains its finiteness (in the light cone gauge) to all orders.

(vii) The infrared finiteness for the case of $n = 2$ (i.e. internal symmetry group SU(2)) comes about because it turns out that the theory possesses a vacuum solution where the internal symmetry group (SU(2)) is spontaneously broken such that all three vector mesons in the theory acquire spontaneously generated masses. Thus no infrared infinities can arise. Namazie has gone further and shown that if $n = 3$ (i.e. the internal symmetry group is (SU(3)), the symmetry breaks down to U(1). His conjecture is that SU(n) may be expected to break down to SU($n - 2$) × U(1) so that $(n - 2)^2$ vector mesons remain massless, leading to the standard infrared problems (familiar in QCD). Results similar to ours were obtained by J G Taylor and A Parkes and P West. (These authors did not work in the light cone gauge.)

Finite supersymmetric field theories ($N = 2$)

In addition to the $N = 4$ theory described so far, there is the set of $N = 2$ supersymmetric Yang–Mills theories which for charge renormalisation are also finite. This comes about because, as Grisaru and Siegel showed in 1982,[10] for β-functions the only surviving infinities are expected to exist for one-loop graphs. All higher loops are finite—provided there exists an extended superfield formalism for such a theory. Such a formalism was indeed recently provided by Howe, Stelle and Townsend.[11] Howe, Stelle and West suggested that if a class of matter multiplets could be found such that their infinities and the infinities from the gauge sector cancelled in the *one-loop* approximation, the β-function would be zero to all orders. There would therefore be no charge renormalisation.

Precisely this happens for SU(n) internal symmetry, provided one takes $2n$ ($N = 2$) matter multiplets in the fundamental representation (or alternatively, one $N = 2$ matter multiplet in the adjoint representation). In an axial or a background gauge the wavefunction renormalisations are also finite. (See Appendix A.)

As I said earlier, we do not know if these theories are physically relevant. Pati and Salam[12] have suggested that such theories may describe preons, the basic constituents of quarks and leptons. Time and experimentation will tell if this conjecture is justified. In the meanwhile, we must salute the physical insight of Dirac's insistence that one must continue looking for finite field theories, rather than be reconciled with ultraviolet infinities—even though these may refer to only a few physical quantities like mass and charge.

Supergravity theories

I have not discussed the supergravity theories so far. When these were invented in 1976 the hope was that they might make infinities of the gravity theory tractable. Such a hope was entertained particularly for extended supergravity theory $N = 8$ ($d = 4$). Unhappily, this hope has not yet been justified, and perhaps never will be. In Appendix B is given the present situation as reviewed by Martin Sohnius.

A new possibility for renormalisation of gravity, however, has opened up from string theories and in particular from closed superstring theories in ten dimensions based on the group $E_8 \times E_8$. Mandelstam in particular has recently given powerful arguments to show that all closed string theories (which include Einstein's gravity) are likely to be finite to all orders. This result will not apply to open string theories which are expected to be renormalisable only.

The string theories are based on two-dimensional Nambu–Goto theories for which Alvarez-Gaumé and D Z Freedman had shown (following the earlier work of Freedman and Townsend) that the $N = 4$ supersymmetric non-linear sigma models are finite. This result has been recently extended by Hull to $N = 1$ (and $N = 2$) supersymmetric non-linear sigma models that are defined on manifolds which are Ricci flat.[13] In the construction of string theories, these basic finite two-dimensional string theories are destined to play an important role.

Personal recollections

I would like to conclude with a number of personal recollections of Dirac.

I once asked Dirac what he thought his greatest contribution to physics was. He said 'The Poisson bracket.' I was surprised because I thought he would speak of the electron equation. When I asked him to elaborate on this, he said that after a long search for the quantum analogue of the Poisson bracket, it struck him that if there are two non-commutative operators, A and B, then the quantity $AB - BA$ would have all the properties of a classical Poisson bracket. However, on the Sunday on which he had made this discovery, he had no texts on dynamics available, and it was an anxious wait until Monday morning when he could finally go to the library and check whether his expression indeed satisfied all conditions a quantum Poisson should.

But with characteristic modesty, he added after a pause that for a long time he felt ecstatic and pleased, till he found essentially the same remark made by Hamilton as a footnote in one of his papers written in the last century.

I once unwisely criticised Eddington in Dirac's presence. My remarks were the result of exasperation with Eddington's *Fundamental Theory*. I believe I said that if Eddington were not a professor at Cambridge, he would not have had his book published. Dirac made the remark (which I have appreciated deeply later): 'One must not judge a man's worth from his poorer work; one must always judge him by the best he has done.'

Once Dirac asked me whether I thought geometrically or algebraically? I said I did not know what he meant, could he tell me how he himself thought. He said his thinking was geometrical. I was taken aback by this because Dirac, with his transformation theory, represented for my generation the algebraic movement in physics par excellence. So I said 'I still don't understand.' He said 'I will ask you a question. How do you picture the de Sitter space?' I said 'I write down the metric and then think about the structure of the expression.' He said, 'Precisely as I thought. You think algebraically as most people from the Indian subcontinent do. I picture, without effort, the de Sitter space as a four-dimensional surface in a five-dimensional space!'

Most of these conversations took place at High Table at St John's College when, every Tuesday, he drove into College in his two-seater for dinner. It was my very great pleasure to sit next to him for several terms at the High Table.

Dirac was always very economical with words. Perhaps one of the best recorded stories is of a newspaper interview that Dirac gave to a Wisconsin journal and which is recounted in the paper by Laurie M Brown and Helmut Rechenberg, 'Paul Dirac and Werner Heisenberg — A Partnership in Science':

The residents of Madison, other than the physicists at the University, learned about Dirac from a local newspaper interview:

I been hearing about a fellow they have up at the U. this spring — a mathematical physicist, or something, they call him — who is pushing Sir Isaac Newton, Einstein and all the others off the front page .... His name is Dirac and he is an Englishman .... So the other afternoon I knocks at the door of Dr Dirac's office in Sterling Hall and a pleasant voice says 'Come in.' And I want to say here and now that this sentence 'come in' was about the longest one emitted by the doctor during our interview.

I found the Doctor a tall youngish-looking man, and the minute I seen the twinkle in his eye I knew I was going to like him . . . he did not seem to be at all busy. Why if I went to interview an American scientist of his class . . . he would blow in carrying a big briefcase, and while he talked he would be pulling lecture notes, proof, reprints, books, manuscripts, or what have you, out of his bag. Dirac is different. He seems to have all the time there is in the world and his heaviest work is looking out the window ....

'Professor,' says I, 'I notice you have quite a few letters in front of your last name. Do they stand for anything in particular?'

'No,' says he.

'. . . Fine,' says I . . . 'Now Doctor will you give me in a few words the low-down on all your investigations?'

'No,' says he.

I went on: 'Do you go to the movies?'

'Yes,' says he.

'When?' says I.

'In 1920 — perhaps also 1930,' says he.

' . . . And now I want to ask you something more: They tell me that you and Einstein are the only ones who can really understand each other . . . Do you ever run across a fellow that even you can't understand?'

'Yes,' says he.

' . . . Do you mind releasing to me who he is?'

'Weyl,' says he.

When at Trieste, we had the idea of celebrating his seventieth birthday. Dirac was most reluctant. In the end, Mrs Dirac convinced him otherwise and he agreed. One of the best evenings in my life was the banquet when in his presence, those present told their recollections of Dirac†.

In Trieste, we constructed 'Scala Dirac'—the Dirac Stairs which takes visitors from the Centre to the Park and is built along the face of a steep slope. These stairs were named Scala Dirac because my secretary once saw Dirac trying to come down that slope. He could not quite negotiate it because it was so steep. Dirac then happily started to slide down. We had to build the stairs and name them after him.

The Centre has now instituted a Dirac medal to be given in his honour on his birthday—8 August—every year, for the highest achievements in theoretical physics. The first medal (1985) was awarded to Ya Zeldovich and E Witten. The second to Y Nambu and A Polyakov.

I will conclude with a story of Dirac and Feynman that conveys, in Feynman's words, what we all thought of Dirac. I was a witness of it at the 1961 Solvay Conference. Those of you who have attended the old Solvay Conferences will know that, at least then, one sat at long tables that were arranged as if one was sitting down to pray. Like a Quaker gathering, there was no fixed agenda; the expectation—seldom belied—was that someone would be moved to start the discussion spontaneously.

At the 1961 Conference I was sitting at one of these long tables next to Dirac, waiting for the session to start, when Feynman came and sat down opposite. Feynman extended his hand towards Dirac and said: 'I am Feynman.' It was clear from his tone that it was the first time they were meeting. Dirac extended his hand and said: 'I am Dirac.' There was silence, which from Feynman was rather remarkable. Then Feynman, like a schoolboy in the presence of a Master, said to Dirac 'It must have felt good to have invented that equation.' And Dirac said 'But that was a long time ago.' Silence again. To break this, Dirac, of all people, asked Feynman, 'What are you yourself working on?' Feynman said 'Meson theories' and Dirac said 'Are you trying to invent a similar equation?' Feynman

†Published in J Mehra's volume *The Physicists' Conception of Nature* (Dordrecht: Reidel, 1973)

said 'That would be very difficult.' And Dirac, in an anxious voice, rejoined 'But one must try.' At that point the conversation finished because the meeting had started.

Appendix: Finiteness of $N = 2$ Theories

The condition for one-loop finiteness which guarantees finiteness to all orders is

$$T(R) = C_2(G)$$

where $T(R)$ and $C_2(G)$ are the Dynkin index of matter multiplets in representation R and the quadratic Casimir operator for the adjoint representation of gauge group G. A complete list of finite field theories can be readily obtained.[14] If matter multiplets are assigned solely to the adjoint representations then the $N = 2$ theory coincides with $N = 4$ theory.

For $SU(n)$ internal symmetry, $N = 2$ supersymmetric Yang–Mills theories with the following representations for matter multiplets are finite:

(i) $2n$ $\square$ for all $SU(n)$;

(ii) $(n - 2)$ $\square$ $+$ $\square\square$ or $[2n - p(n - 2)]$ $\square$ $+ p$ $\begin{array}{c}\square\\\square\end{array}$

  for $SU(n)$ with $n \geqslant 3$;

(iii) $\begin{array}{c}\square\\\square\end{array}$ $+$ $\square\square$ for $SU(n)$ with $n \geqslant 4$;

(iv) 2 $\begin{array}{c}\square\\\square\\\square\end{array}$ or 2 $\square$ $+$ $\begin{array}{c}\square\\\square\\\square\end{array}$ $+$ $\begin{array}{c}\square\\\square\end{array}$ for $SU(6)$;

(v) $\frac{1}{2}(9n - n^2 - 6)$ $\square$ $+$ $\begin{array}{c}\square\\\square\\\square\end{array}$ for $SU(n)$ with $6 \leqslant n \leqslant 8$.

Here the coefficients in front of Young tableaux denote the multiplicities and are positive.

For $SO(n)$ groups, the representations for the matter multiplets of finite field theories are as follows:

(i) $(n-2)$ repetitions of n (fundamental) representation.

(ii) If the matter multiplets are assigned to spinor representations of SO(n), the following four cases, 6(**4**) of SO(5), 5(**8**) of SO(7), 6(**8**) of SO(8) and 4(**16**) of SO(10) satisfy the conditions for finiteness, with multiplicities shown in front of dimensionality.

(iii) The representations with n_f repetitions of the fundamental representation of dimension n and with n_s repetitions of the spinorial representation of dimension $2^{[n/2]}$ for odd n, and $s^{[n/2]-1}$ for even n satisfy the finiteness condition with the following (n_f, n_s) combinations:

SO(5) $(n_f, n_s) = (2,2), (1,4)$

SO(7) $(n_f, n_s) = (4, 1), (3,2), (2,3), (1,4)$

SO(9) $(n_f, n_s) = (5, 1), (3,2), (1,3)$

SO(10) $(n_f, n_s) = (6, 1), (4,2), (2,3)$

SO(12) $(n_f, n_s) = (6,1), (2,2)$

SO(14) $(n_f, n_s) = (4,1)$

The representations of matter multiplets allowed for the Sp($2m$) group are:

(i) $(2m+2)$ repetitions of $2m$ fundamental representation,

(ii) four repetitions of $2m$ and one second-rank antisymmetric representation of dimension $m(2m-1)$.

To give more details of $N=2$ theories in exceptional groups, we use the following representations of matter multiplets from $N=2$ finite field theories:

(i)   four times **27** in E_6

(ii) three times **56** in E_7

(iii) three times **26** in F_4

(iv) four times **7** in G_2.

It is interesting to note that the only representation satisfying the finiteness condition for E_8 is the adjoint representation. Thus finiteness for E_8 gauge requires the $N=4$ theory.

References

1 Namazie M A, Strathdee J and Salam A 1983 *Phys. Rev.* D **28** 1481
2 Avdeev L V, Tarasov O V and Vladimirov A A 1980 *Phys. Lett.* **96B** 94
3 Grisaru M T, Roček M and Siegel W 1980 *Phys. Rev. Lett.* **45** 1063
4 Caswell W and Zanon D 1981 *Phys. Lett.* **100B** 152
5 S Ferrara and B Zumino unpublished work
6 Sohnius M and West P 1981 *Phys. Lett.* **100B** 245
7 Stelle K 1982 in *Quantum Structure of Space and Time* ed M J Duff and C J Isham (Cambridge: Cambridge University Press) p. 337.5
8 Mandelstam S 1983 *Nucl. Phys.* B **213**; 1982 *21st Int. Conf. on High Energy Physics, Paris*
9 Brink L *et al* 1983 *Phys. Lett.* **123B** 323
10 Grisaru M T and Siegel W 1982 *Nucl. Phys.* B **201** 292
11 Howe P, Stelle K and Townsend P 1983 *Phys. Lett.* **124B** 55
12 Pati J and Salam A 1984 *Nucl. Phys.* B **214** 109 V
13 Freedman D Z and Townsend P 1981 *Nucl. Phys.* B **177** 282; Alvarez-Gaumé L and Freedman D Z 1981 *Comm. Math. Phys.* **80** 443; Alvarez-Gaumé L and Freedman D Z 1980 *Phys. Rev.* D **15** 846; Alvarez-Gaumé L, Freedman D Z and Mukhi S 1985 *Ann. Phys., NY* **134** 85
14 Koh I G and Rajpoot S 1984 *Phys. Lett.* **135B** 397

Fourier Analysis
and Generalised Functions

James Lighthill

As the individual who in 1969 succeeded Paul Dirac in the Lucasian Chair of Mathematics, which he had held for four decades, I have been asked to contribute to this meeting by saying something about Dirac and mathematics. Although many aspects of this theme might be surveyed in relation to a mathematician as diversely skilled, and as innovative, as Dirac, I have ventured to choose one particular aspect of his mathematical work which aroused my curiosity from the moment in 1941 when I first got to know Dirac through being one of the, in wartime, very small class of persons attending his Part III lectures on quantum mechanics. Simultaneously I was attending G H Hardy's Part III lectures on Fourier analysis and it was the creative tension between the extremely different approaches to that subject pursued by these two individuals, both mathematically brilliant, which stimulated me to wonder whether any reconciliation of their points of view would be possible; such a reconciliation as I did indeed much later venture to offer in my little 1958 book with the same title as this lecture.

In this lecture title 'Fourier analysis and generalised functions' I have put Fourier analysis first, even though Dirac's name became attached to a particular generalised function which is still often called the Dirac delta function $\delta(x)$, because the use of the generalised function $\delta(x)$ as such does in fact date back to the 1882 article of Gustav Kirchhoff '*Zur Theorie der Lichtstrahlen*'.[1] Kirchhoff, indeed, used the notation $\delta(x)$ for a sort of notional limit of a sequence of functions

$$\delta_n(x) = (n/\pi)^{1/2} e^{-nx^2} \qquad (n = 1, 2, 3, \dots) \qquad (1)$$

some of which are plotted in figure 1; while Dirac's introduction of $\delta(x)$ in the third chapter of his famous 1930 book *The Principles of Quantum Mechanics* adopts essentially the same approach. Another forerunner in the use of such functions had been the electrical engineer Oliver Heaviside in his 1892 article 'On operations in physical mathematics';[2] and Dirac, with his electrical engineering background, may be regarded as particularly likely to have come across Heaviside's ideas at some time. Nevertheless, even though Heaviside had himself performed some Fourier analysis on such functions, it is fair to claim for Dirac that it was in his confident, easy and flexible application of all the main operations of Fourier analysis to delta functions and to other generalised functions that his special contribution to analytical attitudes had been made.

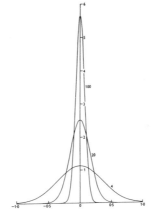

Figure 1   Three members of the sequence of functions $\delta_n(x)$ defined by equation (1); the number n (for $n = 4, 20, 100$) being attached to the graph of the nth function.

Certainly for myself, as a Cambridge undergraduate back in 1941, there seemed to be a most profound contrast between the attitudes to Fourier analysis exhibited within the same Lecture Room B in the Arts School when Hardy occupied it and when Dirac did. Hardy emphasised the need for rigorous proof of results. To reinforce this message he paraded large numbers of highly imposing counter-examples to almost every conceivable plausible, yet unproved, conjecture. He *also* reinforced it by winning us to admire not only the aesthetic charm but also the compelling force of the rigorous proofs of established theorems which he gave. Results so proved could be used with real confidence, unlike any of the plausible conjectures to which such clear and cogent counter-examples existed.

What a contrast between the sceptical Hardy and the intuitive Dirac who transfixed you with his clear, far-seeing gaze and confidently pointed out that the Fourier transform of 1 was obviously $\delta(x)$; or that the Fourier series with unit coefficients

$$\sum_{n=-\infty}^{\infty} \cos(2n\pi x) \tag{2}$$

must evidently represent $\delta(x)$; or, more precisely, represent the *periodic* function of unit period which coincides with $\delta(x)$ in a period spanning the origin; that is,

$$\sum_{m=-\infty}^{\infty} \delta(x-m). \tag{3}$$

Similarly, one could unhesitatingly equate the differentiated forms of (2) and (3), putting

$$\sum_{n=-\infty}^{\infty} (-2n\pi) \sin(2n\pi x) = \sum_{m=-\infty}^{\infty} \delta'(x-m) \tag{4}$$

where the differentiated delta function $\delta'(x)$ must be thought of as a sort of notional limit of the sequence of functions

$$\delta_n'(x) = -2nx(n/\pi)^{1/2} e^{-nx^2} \tag{5}$$

some of which are plotted in figure 2.

Now you must not imagine, of course, that Hardy would have felt the slightest distaste for either of the trigonometrical series (2) or (4) simply because neither of them was a *convergent* series. Hardy was indeed a profound authority on series which did not converge and his admirable monograph *Divergent Series* listed and expounded all the special methods that existed (such as the Cesàro and Abel methods) for attaching a precise meaning to the sum of any divergent series—defined not as the limit of its partial sums (which is the definition for a convergent series) but as a limit of weighted means of its partial sums. The series (2) was in this sense summable if not everywhere then at any rate 'almost everywhere' (*presque partout* or p.p.) in the precise sense which analysts use;

its value being zero p.p. and indeed zero for any x which was not an integer. The mere 'countable' set, a set of measure zero, for which summability failed was even not regarded very seriously (although expression (3), of course, identifies it as containing the essence of the series' behaviour).

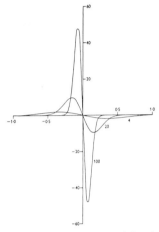

Figure 2   Functions $\delta'_n(x)$ in the sequence defined by equation (5); being the derivatives of the functions graphed in figure 1.

Hardy with his customary clarity and power used his lectures to expound summability methods and their marked relevance for Fourier analysis. Although the Fourier series of an integrable function may fail to *converge* even at a point where the function is continuous, nevertheless it is always summable (by, say, the Abel method) at such a point to the value of the function. Furthermore, at a 'point of jump', where the function tends to different limiting values from above and below, its Fourier series is always summable to their mean, and in such a way that the so-called Gibbs phenomenon is suppressed. Also, the function's Fourier series differentiated term-by-term is necessarily summable by the Abel method to that function's differential coefficient at any point where the latter exists.

From some alternative points of view, on the other hand, 'good old convergence' was stressed by Hardy as having its advantages.

These included Cantor's uniqueness theorem: that a pair of trigonometrical series which *converged* to the same sum, except possibly in a countable set, must be identical series. The same result can be stated more simply than this, in terms of the difference between the series. That series, if it converges to *zero*, except possibly in a countable set, must have all its coefficients zero.

No such result applies with regard to summability, of course; for example, the very simple series (2) is summable to zero except only when x belongs to a countable set (that of the integers). The series (4) is even more interesting in this regard: it is summable to zero whenever x is not an integer, yet when x *is* an integer all its terms are individually zero, so that its sum as calculated by any method is zero! Thus, such a trigonometrical series can be summable to zero at *every* point without its coefficients being identically zero. That result is, of course, by no means incompatible with the representation on the right-hand side of (4); thus, figure 2 shows that for any particular x whatsoever, the *limit* of these functions $\delta_n'(x)$ is zero; yet this fact once again conceals the true essence of the series' behaviour.

Physicists, of course, need uniqueness. When they approach an equation $Lf = 0$ (where the operator L is linear but in other respects may be highly complicated) by substituting a trigonometrical series for f, they need to be able to determine the coefficients of that series on the assumption that the operator L applied to each term is separately zero. On the one hand this requires that differentiation (and any other operations involved in L) can be applied term-by-term to the series. This assumption may as we have seen be justified for the Abel summability approach; yet with the convergence approach it is completely false. Simultaneously, a physicist must feel confident that, if the trigonometrical series for f, after it has been thus modified by applying L to each term, is identically zero, then the individual coefficients in this modified series are zero (which enables those in the series for f itself to be determined). Yet this assumption, while correct on the assumption of *convergence* for the modified series, becomes totally false (as we have seen) for the summability approach.

The combination of properties which a physicist must need, then, which certainly include *both* uniqueness *and* term-by-term differentiability, was completely absent in both the summability and the convergence theories of Fourier analysis. Yet the intuitive mind of Dirac was confidently registering that, in fact, every single property (including these) which a physicist might need was present in a theory which applied Fourier analysis to a properly extended category of functions. Actually, of course, Dirac was much more *frequently* concerned with Fourier integrals than with Fourier series, but I have been limiting myself to Fourier series in this short talk merely to keep everything as simple as possible.

Back in 1941 it seemed impossible to a 17-year-old student, exposed at the same time to Dirac's grand certainties based above all (perhaps) on the massive successes which his physical theories had had, and to Hardy's equally grand scepticism based on his own and other analysts' imposing successes in providing counter-examples to almost every plausible conjecture, to foresee where the truth might lie. Yet the truth of the matter was at that time being uncovered in the work of Laurent Schwartz, which first saw the light of day in a 1945 article 'Généralisation de la notion de fonction';[3] and, later, was magisterially expounded in his 1950 monograph *Théorie des Distributions*. Schwartz proved that indeed all the Fourier-analysis properties desired by physicists are possessed by a properly extended category of functions, which he called distributions. He actually developed the theory in a manner that had been anticipated *in part* in the 1936 work of the Russian mathematician S L Sobolev, in terms of the definition of a distribution as a linear functional on a function space of so-called test functions.[4] The proofs utilised extensive and complicated machinery from the topology of function spaces, but they were accurate and conclusive.

Thus, Dirac's intuition was demonstrated as having been right all along! Nevertheless, the body of ideas underlying the new definitions was felt by some physicists, and by at least one applied mathematician, to appear just a little remote and indirect compared with Dirac's very straightforward intuitive approach. I was personally delighted, then, when George Temple began to produce an alternative approach,[5] founded on an idea put forward in 1948 by the Polish mathematician Mikusiński,[6] which seemed to offer a body of much more direct definitions and several quite simple proofs. Above all, they were based on seeing any generalised function as simply *defined* by a sequence of well behaved test functions or 'good' functions (as in figures 1 and 2) which was a weakly convergent or 'regular' sequence. This definition was accompanied by a test for determining which pairs of regular sequences define the same generalised function. That idea, while of course being a special case of a standard and important general idea in topology, is readily intelligible by inexperienced students as a natural generalisation of the normal idea of a function. A particularly satisfactory feature is that the derivatives of the sequence always define the derivative of the generalised function; and, similarly, the Fourier transforms of the sequence always define the generalised function's Fourier transform, which always satisfies Fourier's inversion theorem.

I enjoyed, in the mid-1950s, working to lay the ghost of my conflicting loyalties towards Dirac and towards Hardy by compiling an account which would give rigorous proofs of each result which would be as simple as possible (in the Hardy manner), while demonstrating for those functions of a single variable to which I confined myself that all the properties needed by physicists are as triumphantly true as Dirac had postulated.[7] Later, Douglas Jones published a similar book extending all the results to functions of many variables.[8]

In the limited sphere of Fourier series to which this talk has been mainly confined, the properties proved include the following. Any trigonometrical series whose nth coefficient tends to zero after first being divided by *some* positive power of n must necessarily converge to a generalised function. Conversely, any generalised function is identically equal to the sum of its Fourier series, with the coefficients (which necessarily have the property just mentioned) defined in a manner which is a natural extension of the classical one. Next, differentiation and the other linear operations of analysis can be applied term-by-term to such series; and, finally, the uniqueness property that any trigonometrical series whose sum is identically zero must have zero coefficients is derived in an elegantly simple manner on the definitions of this theory. That is as far as I will take the matter now; but, in the light of what I have said, you will understand why I dedicate this talk as I dedicated my little book 'to Paul Dirac, who saw that it must be true; to Laurent Schwartz, who proved it; and to George Temple, who showed how simple it could be made'. And I do this with a special loving backward look towards my great predecessor in the Lucasian Professorship of Mathematics.

References

1 Kirchhoff G 1882 Zur Theorie der Lichtstrahlen *Sitzungsber. d. preuss. Akad. Wiss.* **II** 641–69
2 Heaviside O 1892 On operations in physical mathematics *Proc. R. Soc.* A **52** 504–29
3 Schwartz L 1945 Généralisation de la notion de fonction *Ann. Univ. Grenoble* **21** 57–74
4 Sobolev S L 1936 Méthode nouvelle à resoudre le problème de Cauchy *Mat. Sbornik* **1** 39–72
5 Temple G 1955 The theory of generalized functions *Proc. R. Soc.* A **228** 175–90
6 Mikusiński J 1948 Sur la méthode de généralisation de M. Laurent Schwartz *Fundam. Math.* **35** 235–9
7 Lighthill M J 1958 *Introduction to Fourier Analysis and Generalised Functions* (Cambridge: Cambridge University Press)
8 Jones D S 1966 *Generalised Functions* (London: McGraw-Hill)

Magnetic Monopoles

Peter Goddard

I have been asked to give an account of Dirac's work on magnetic monopoles and its seminal influence. Dirac wrote two papers on magnetic monopoles: 'Quantised singularities in the electromagnetic field' published in 1931 in the *Proceedings of the Royal Society*[1] and 'The theory of magnetic monopoles' published in the *Physical Review*[2] in 1948. In these papers he argued that quantum mechanics 'does not preclude the existence of isolated magnetic poles. On the contrary the present formalism, when developed without the imposition of arbitrary restrictions, leads inevitably to wave functions whose only physical interpretation is the motion of an electron in the field of a single pole.'[1]

In his introduction to the 1931 paper, Dirac commented on the progressive relationship between mathematics and theoretical physics: 'the steady progress of physics requires for its theoretical formulation a mathematics that gets continually more advanced'. But, he went on to point out, not only more advanced but also more abstract, in a way which was not anticipated in the nineteenth century. Non-Euclidean geometry was needed for relativity, non-commutative algebra for quantum theory. The fundamental problems then outstanding, which in fact are (in his sense at least) still with us, would, he thought, 'presumbly require a more drastic revision of our concepts than any that have gone before'. So drastic, in fact, that the approach that succeeded with quantum theory, of formulating experimental data directly in mathematical terms, might well fail and that the best approach for the theoretical worker might be 'to employ all of the resources of pure mathematics in attempts to perfect and generalise the mathematical formalism that forms the existing basis of theoretical physics, and *after* each success in this direction to try to interpret the new mathematical features in terms of physical entities'. Dirac suggested that his then recent work[3] on the negative energy states of the electron, which he explained necessitated the existence of 'anti-electrons' (thus making the prediction which may be seen as the birth of elementary particle physics), might 'possibly be regarded as a small step according to this general scheme of advance', and that his work on magnetic monopoles might be comparable.

Arguably, theoretical physicists have been following Dirac's advice. The various component theoretical ideas put together in the spontaneously broken gauge theories, which now clearly provide a unified description of the weak and electromagnetic interactions, and may possibly encompass much more, have received their mathematical development outside the context of their successful physical application. And other theoretical approaches, whose physical relevance is still not proved, such as supersymmetry and supergravity, or relativistic string theories, may also be seen as attempts to go along the path Dirac outlined.

Although he commented on the importance of the development of mathematics for the advancement of physics, he did not comment on the seminal influence that physical ideas and problems can have as stimuli in pure mathematics. So much of his work, and in particular the work on magnetic monopoles, can be seen as prime examples of this. In the work we are to discuss can be found the principal seed of the exciting developments, especially during the last ten years, of an extremely fruitful two-way interaction between field theory in theoretical physics on the one hand and topology and modern geometry on the other.

Of course, Dirac was not unconcerned about the absence of observed magnetic monopoles. Since he first wrote there have been isolated candidates for monopole observations but none have subsequently received definitive confirmation.[4] Although, in 1931, Dirac had said that 'one would be surprised if Nature had made no use of it' [i.e. the possibility of accommodating magnetic monopoles within the framework of quantum mechanics], in 1981 he sent a message to a conference organised at the International Centre for Theoretical Physics in Trieste to mark the fiftieth anniversary of his paper, saying 'I am inclined now to believe that monopoles do not exist. So many years have gone by without any encouragement from the experimental side.'[5]

In spite of the lack of experimental encouragement, Dirac's ideas provided the stimulus for an enormous amount of theoretical work. By 1981 about 1800 papers on monopoles could be listed[6] and since then interest has abated little. More than half these publications have occurred since 1974 when 't Hooft[7] and Polyakov[8] independently observed that certain spontaneous broken gauge theories had (classical) solutions which have the natural interpretation of being magnetic monopoles. Although Dirac's monopoles are point singularities whilst these are smooth solutions, at large distance they look just the same. We shall return to the occurrence of magnetic monopoles in gauge theories, but let us first consider the results of Dirac's 1931 paper.

Dirac showed that the condition for the consistency of the quantum mechanics of a particle with electric charge q, moving in the given background field of a magnetic monopole of strength g, was that

$$\frac{qg}{2\pi\hbar}$$

must be an integer. This is *Dirac's quantisation condition*. It has some immediate and fascinating consequences. Firstly, it provides a potential explanation of the quantisation of electric charge, the mysterious fact that particles as different as the proton and the electron appear experimentally to have electric charges of exactly the same magnitude and that all observed electric charges are multiples of this basic unit. Apart from recent candidate explanations within the so-called grand unified theories of strong, weak and electromagnetic interactions, to which we shall subsequently refer, no other reasons for this striking observation have been found. The only way for Dirac's quantisation condition to be satisfied is for each electric charge q and magnetic charge g to be multiples of some basic units q_0, g_0 of electric and magnetic charges which themselves satisfy Dirac's condition:

$$\frac{q_0 g_0}{2\pi\hbar} = N$$

(i.e. an integer). (One might expect $N = 1$ in the absence of any argument to the contrary.)

Secondly, Dirac's condition tells us something about the ratio of the strengths of electric to magnetic forces. Measured at similar distances, the ratio of the force between basic units of electric charge to that between basic units of magnetic charge is

$$\frac{q_0^2}{g_0^2} = \frac{4}{N^2} \left(\frac{q_0^2}{4\pi\hbar}\right)^2 = \frac{4\alpha^2}{N^2}$$

where $\alpha = q_0^2/4\pi\hbar \approx 1/137$ is the fine structure constant. The experimental value of α indicates a quantitative asymmetry between electric and magnetic poles which Dirac suggested[1] might be the reason why the latter might bind more tightly in opposite pairs, so accounting for the lack of observation of isolated magnetic poles.

A somewhat naive argument which leads to Dirac's conditon is the following. Consider the classical motion of a particle of mass m in electric charge q in the field

$$B = \frac{-q}{4\pi r^2} \hat{r}$$

of a magnetic monopole of strength g fixed at the origin. The equation of motion is

$$m\ddot{r} = q\dot{r} \wedge B.$$

For such a motion, because the force is not central, the ordinary orbital angular momentum $mr \wedge \dot{r}$ is not conserved; in fact

$$\frac{d}{dt}(mr \wedge \dot{r}) = r \wedge m\ddot{r} = \frac{d}{dt}\left(\frac{qg}{4\pi}\hat{r}\right).$$

Thus the quantity

$$J = mr \wedge \dot{r} - \frac{qg}{4\pi}\hat{r}$$

is conserved instead, a result obtained in 1896 by Poincaré.[9] In fact J exceeds the orbital angular momentum by a quantity equal to the angular momentum of the electromagnetic field generated by the system of electric and magnetic charges. Now, in quantum mechanics, the components of angular momentum can only take values which are multiples of $\frac{1}{2}\hbar$, a result that follows directly from the algebra that the relation between commutators and Poisson brackets forces these components to satisfy. If we assume that, for this system, this condition applies to the components of J and that, in particular, we can apply it to its radial component, we obtain

$$\hat{r} \cdot J = -\frac{qg}{4\pi} = -\frac{n}{2}\hbar$$

for some integer n, and this is precisely Dirac's condition.[10] The points we have slid over can be justified by demonstrating that Dirac's canonical quantisation procedure leads to the components of J satisfying the angular momentum algebra and by showing this holds for suitably moving axes.

Dirac's argument[1] concerned the phase ambiguity in the wavefunction and can be rephrased in its essentials as follows. The Schrödinger equation is changed from the free particle equation

$$\frac{1}{2m}(-i\hbar \nabla)^2\psi = i\hbar \frac{\partial \psi}{\partial t}$$

to

$$\frac{1}{2m}(-i\hbar \nabla - qA)^2\psi + q\varphi\psi = i\hbar \frac{\partial \psi}{\partial t}$$

if the particle has electric charge q and is placed in an electromagnetic field

$$B = \nabla \wedge A \qquad E = -\nabla \varphi - \dot{A}.$$

The potentials occurring in the Schrödinger equation are not unique but can be changed by a gauge transformation

$$A \to A' = A + \nabla \chi$$

$$\varphi \to \varphi' = \varphi - \dot{\chi}$$

without changing the fields E and B. The Schrödinger equation in the new gauge

$$\frac{1}{2m}(-i\hbar \nabla - qA')^2\psi' + q\varphi'\psi' = i\hbar \frac{\partial \psi'}{\partial t}$$

should give the same physical results as the Schrödinger equation in the original gauge. This follows because the wavefunctions in the two equations are related by the gauge transformation

$$\psi \to \psi' = \exp(ie\chi)\psi$$

where $e = q/\hbar$.

Now consider the Schrödinger equation for the particle in the field of a magnetic monopole at the origin. Such a field cannot be described by a single vector potential A, for if it could the magnetic charge would have to vanish, as we see by calculating the magnetic flux through any surface Σ containing the origin:

$$g = \oiint_\Sigma B \cdot dS = \oiint_\Sigma \nabla \wedge A \cdot dS$$

which vanishes by Stokes's theorem. But, exploiting the gauge invariance of Schrödinger's equation, we can circumvent this difficulty by using different gauges in the 'northern' and 'southern' hemispheres, with corresponding wavefunctions and potentials related by a gauge transformation:

$$\psi_N = \exp(ie\chi)\psi_S \qquad A_N = A_S + \nabla\chi.$$

This will be satisfactory provided that both ψ_S and ψ_N are well defined single-valued functions. This is not totally straightforward because it is easy to see that the gauge function χ cannot itself be single valued; it must change on going once around the 'equator' $\mathscr{C}$, by an amount equal to the magnetic charge g, since

$$g = \oiint_\Sigma B \cdot dS$$

$$= \int\int_{\Sigma_N} (\nabla \wedge A_N) \cdot dS + \int\int_{\Sigma_S} (\nabla \wedge A_S) \cdot dS$$

$$= \oint_\mathscr{C} (A_N - A_S) \cdot dr$$

$$= \oint_\mathscr{C} \nabla\chi \cdot dr = [\chi]_\mathscr{C}$$

the change in χ on going once around $\mathscr{C}$. (Here Σ_N and Σ_S denote the 'northern' and 'southern' hemispheres, respectively.) Fortunately, single valuedness of the wavefunctions requires that $\exp(ie\chi)$ rather than χ itself be single valued; thus

$$\exp(ie[\chi]_\mathscr{C}) = \exp(iqg/\hbar) = 1$$

which is precisely the Dirac quantisation condition.

Dirac put his argument somewhat differently. For one thing he took the point of view that it was natural to have path dependent phase factors of the form

$$\exp\left(ie \int_{r_0}^{r} A \cdot dr\right) = \exp(ie\chi)$$

and that this leads naturally to the ability to accommodate monopoles, which has surely not been overlooked by Nature. Also, rather than use two overlapping gauges, one in the 'northern' hemisphere, and one in the 'southern', as here, he used one gauge which could be employed at all but one point on any given sphere. The union of these points for different spheres formed a line, extending from the origin to infinity, which is called the 'Dirac string'. Dirac thought that the wavefunction would have to vanish on this 'string' but this can be avoided by use of two gauges, as we have done, showing that the string has no physical significance. As we go around the string, or around the 'equator' in the way we have phrased it, the phase factor $\exp(ie\chi)$ goes an integral number of times round the unit circle in the complex plane, describing a closed loop

$$\exp(iegs) \qquad 0 \leqslant s \leqslant 1.$$

This illustrates the essentially topological nature of Dirac's quantisation condition.

Our discussion has referred mainly to Dirac's 1931 paper. In his second paper he extended the theory of magnetic monopoles in a number of ways, in particular from the non-relativistic to the relativistic case and to a number of electric and magnetic charges in interaction.

The gauge transformations on wavefunctions that we have been using have taken their values in the complex numbers of unit modulus, i.e. the Abelian group U(1), which is the gauge group of electromagnetism. In the last 20 years it has been realised that the U(1) gauge theory of electromagnetism is only a part of a larger gauge theory, containing at least the Salam–Weinberg[11] unified theory of weak and electromagnetic interactions, for which the gauge group is enlarged from U(1) to a group with structure SU(2) × U(1) (locally). Presumably, the gauge group H of the theory also contains an SU(3) 'colour' gauge group, the gauge bosons of which (i.e. the analogues of the photon) are the gluons which mediate the strong interactions. Dirac's arguments immediately generalise to this wider context, which was totally unenvisaged at the time of his original paper. This ease of generalisation or width of applicability, a hallmark of his arguments, is a measure of their depth. For a non-Abelian gauge group H, the magnetic charge g would be replaced by a Hermitian matrix $\mathbf{g}$, a generator of the group but, with this change made, we would still get a closed loop in the gauge group H, and we see that the structure of monopoles is connected with the topology of such closed loops in H. The Dirac quantisation condition becomes

$$\exp(i e \mathbf{g}) = 1.$$

As a consequence, in the presence of these other gauge fields, the Dirac condition does not have to be satisfied by the electromagnetic charges alone. In a realistic model one might find that whilst a particle with only electric charge q satisfies

$$\exp(i q g / \hbar) = 1$$

a particle emitting colour flux as well would have

$$\exp(i q g / \hbar) = \exp(\pm 2\pi i / 3).$$

In this way the Dirac condition provides an explanation for the fractional charges of coloured particles such as quarks[12].

In current theories the gauge symmetry group H manifested in Nature, which is supposed to contain a group with (local) structure $U(1) \times SU(2) \times SU(3)$, is not the original symmetry of hypothetical fundamental equations. This is a larger gauge group $G \supset H$ which is spontaneously broken down to H, just as the local rotational invariance of the laws of physics in a magnetic material is spontaneously broken to an axial symmetry by the direction of magnetisation. At large distances one sees only H but at small distances G comes into play. It is in the context of such 'grand unified theories' that, under certain assumptions about the structure of H and G, smooth magnetic monopole solutions of the 't Hooft–Polyakov type are inevitable.

Unlike the point monopoles of Dirac, these solutions, being smooth, have calculable properties such as mass and magnetic charge. The magnetic charge in fact satisfies the Dirac condition relative to the electric charges that we expect to find in the theory on quantisation. It is not obvious why this should inevitably be so but if one checks it turns out that it is. If it were not, these theories would be (at least superficially) inconsistent. It seems that there must be some deep mechanism ensuring this consistency which we have yet to understand. The calculated masses of these solutions, using the conventional physical interpretation of parameters in the theory are in excess of $10^{16}\,\mathrm{GeV}/c^2$ but the lack of observed monopoles has still caused difficulties for these theories.

One of the claims for grand unified theories is that they explain electric charge quantisation by means of a symmetry linking baryons and leptons. In fact they provide such an explanation if and only if they have a certain structure of symmetry breaking from the original gauge group G to the manifest gauge group H, and this structure is precisely that which ensures the existence of magnetic monopole solutions, another aspect of an apparently deep consistency in the structure of grand unified theories.

The work of 't Hooft[7] and Polyakov[8] and its topological character proved a stimulus for the study of monopoles[14] and other topological structures in field theories, in particular gauge theories, for example instantons.[15] This has led on to fruitful interactions between physics and mathematics.[16]

Thus we see the continuing seminal influence of this one part of Dirac's work in some of the most topical areas of theoretical physics and pure mathematics. For 40 years, Dirac's work on monopoles was regarded by most theoretical physicists as a backwater, but it has come to be re-evaluated as a development of fundamental importance.

References

1   Dirac P A M 1931 *Proc. R. Soc.* A **133** 60
2   Dirac P A M 1948 *Phys. Rev.* **74** 817
3   Dirac P A M 1930 *Proc. R. Soc.* A **126** 360
4   See for example Giacomelli G 1982 in *Magnetic Monopoles* ed R A Carrigan and W P Trower (New York: Plenum) p. 41
5   Dirac P A M 1982 in *Monopoles in Quantum Field Theory* ed N S Craigie *et al* (Singapore: World Scientific)
6   Ruzicka J and Zelov V P 1981 *Dubna Preprint* D2-81-675
7   't Hooft G 1974 *Nucl. Phys.* B **79** 276
8   Polyakov A M 1974 *JETP Lett.* **20** 194

9   Poincaré H 1896 *C.R. Acad. Sci., Paris* **123** 530

10   Saha M N 1936 *Ind. J. Phys.* 145; 1949 *Phys. Rev.* **75** 1968

11   Salam A 1968 in *Proc. 8th Nobel Symp.: Elementary Particle Theory* ed N Svartholm (New York: Wiley) p. 337; Weinberg S 1967 *Phys. Rev. Lett.* **19** 1264

12   Corrigan E and Olive D 1976 *Nucl. Phys.* B **110** 236

13   Olive D 1980 in *Unification of the Fundamental Particle Interactions* ed S Ferrara *et al* (New York: Plenum) p. 451

14   For reviews see for example: Coleman S in *Proc. 1975 Int. School of Subnuclear Physics* ed A Zichichi (New York: Plenum) p. 297; Goddard P and Olive D 1978 *Rep. Prog. Phys.* **41** 1357; Coleman S in *Proc. 1981 Int. School of Subnuclear Physics* ed A Zichichi (New York: Plenum) p. 21

15   Belavin A, Polyakov A, Schwartz A and Tyupkin Y 1975 *Phys. Lett.* **59B** 85

16   See for example Atiyah M F 1979 *Geometry of Yang–Mills Fields* (Pisa); Freed D S and Uhlenbeck K K 1984 *Instantons and Four-Manifolds* (MSRI Publications 1) (New York: Springer)

Constrained Dynamics

J G Taylor

Paul Dirac's name is justly entered into the Hall of Fame of theoretical physics for his work on the construction of quantum mechanics, for helping create quantum field theory, for discovering his famous relativistic wave equation for the electron, for the concept of the magnetic monopole, and for developing and using the 'Dirac delta function' with such exquisite mastery. You have already heard about these fundamental contributions from others at the conference. Yet for those working in the most recent developments of fundamental theories of the forces of nature—the gauge field theories—it is necessary constantly to use mathematical tools and concepts associated with yet another area in which Paul Dirac made a fundamental contribution, that of constrained dynamics. It is that work which I will try to describe here, and I will especially indicate the far-reaching concepts which Paul Dirac singled out in his powerful and elegant way [1,2,3] as the crucial features; they are constantly being used and elaborated on today.

The areas of modern theoretical physics in which constrained dynamics is essential at both the classical and quant level are a veritable 'who's who' of modern approaches to the forces of nature. Thus besides particle mechanics as the simplest case of dynamical systems which may be constrained (simple since these systems only possess a finite number of degrees of freedom) we have the intrinsically constrained dynamical field theories of:

> Electromagnetism
> Yang–Mills non-Abelian gauge theories
> Einsteinian (more generally geometric) gravity
> Supersymmetric Yang–Mills theories

Supergravity
Strings (both bosonic and fermionic)
Superstrings
Membranes (or bags)
Submanifolds

The broad range of constrained dynamical systems used or postulated as being used by Nature indicates the need to have a broad-based approach to the problems met in analysing such systems especially as far as their true degrees of freedom are concerned. Let me add that, to my mind, the best introductory reference to the subject of constrained dynamics is still Paul Dirac's lectures at Yeshiva University,[4] with Kurt Sundermeyer's more recent review,[5] including over three hundred references, describing more recent work, and that of Marmo, Mukunda and Samuel[6] being helpful from a more geometric viewpoint.

I will begin by describing briefly how constraints arise in a dynamical system with only a finite number of degrees of freedom, which latter I will denote by $q_1, \ldots, q_N$, or collectively q (problems which may arise on extension of these results to field theories with an infinite number of degrees of freedom may be non-trivial; I refer to Sundermeyer[5] (Ch. II, §4) for details on this). We assume the dynamics of the system is described by a Lagrangian function $L(q, \dot{q})$, where $\dot{q} = dq/dt$, with t the time. In the usual fashion, momentum is defined by

$$p_r = \partial L/\partial \dot{q}_r. \tag{1}$$

If the rank R of the matrix $\partial^2 L/\partial \dot{q}_r \partial \dot{q}_s$ is less than N, it will not be possible to solve (1) for $(N-R)$ of the $\dot{q}_r$ and replace them by the associated momenta. If we substitute the solutions for the first R of the $\dot{q}_r$ from (1) into the right-hand side of (1) for all r, the first R equations will reduce to $p_r = p_r$, but the later equations with $R+1 \leqslant r \leqslant N$ appear to depend on the unsolved — for $\dot{q}_r$ unless these equations do not depend at all on these latter variables. Since the latter must happen there will therefore exist $(N-R)$ constraints which may be written in the form

$$\varphi_r = p_r - g_r(q, p_\alpha) = 0 \tag{2}$$

where $R + 1 \leqslant r \leqslant N$, and $1 \leqslant \alpha \leqslant R$. It is the set of equations (2) which are the constraints, and indicate that only a subset Γ_p of the whole phase space of points $\{q, p\}$ is accessible to the dynamical system. It is this reduction of the phase space which furthermore causes severe difficulties in quantisation.

The Lagrangian aspect of the above Hamiltonian (phase space) aspect of constraints is the inability to solve completely the Euler–Lagrange equations of motion

$$\frac{\mathrm{d}}{\mathrm{d}t} \left(\frac{\partial L}{\partial \dot{q}_r} \right) = \frac{\partial L}{\partial q_r}. \tag{3}$$

For we may write the left-hand side of (3) as

$$(\partial^2 L / \partial \dot{q}_r \, \partial \dot{q}_s) \, \ddot{q}_s + (\partial^2 L / \partial \dot{q}_r \, \partial q_s) \dot{q}_s. \tag{4}$$

The result follows since the matrix multiplying $\ddot{q}$ in the first term in (4) is non-invertible for a constrained dynamical system. In particular this indicates that a general motion of the system will depend on $(N - R)$ unknown functions $\dot{q}_r(t)$, with $R + 1 \leqslant r \leqslant N$. This feature is at the origin of the property of 'gauge invariance', a notion crucial to the modern analysis of gauge field theories.

The simplest example of a constrained dynamical system is that of the point particle in d dimensions with action $S = m \int \mathrm{d}s = m \int (\mathrm{d}x^\mu / \mathrm{d}s)^2 \, \mathrm{d}s$. Then $p^\mu = m \, \mathrm{d}x^\mu / \mathrm{d}s / [(\mathrm{d}u^\mu / \mathrm{d}s)^2]^{1/2}$, so that p^μ satisfies the constraint $p_2 = p^\mu p_\mu = m^2$. This constraint can be used to deduce the Klein–Gordon equation on considering a field theory of point particles, an aspect we will not follow up here except to note its importance in modern work.

In the case of the simplest constrained field theory, that of electromagnetism introduced by Maxwell in the early 1860s, the fundamental dynamical variables may be considered as the electromagnetic potentials A_μ in the Lagrange density $\partial_{[\mu} A_{\nu]} \cdot \partial^{[\mu} A^{\nu]}$ (with $\mu = 0, 1, 2, 3$). We see that this Lagrangian does not contain $\dot{A}_0$, so resulting in the constraint $\pi_{A_0} = 0$ for the momentum associated with the potential component A_0.

In order to analyse constrained dynamical systems, Dirac[1] introduced two crucial ideas.

(i) The notion of *weak* equality compared to *strong* equality for functions on the constrained phase space Γ_p. Thus the function $F(q, p)$ on Γ_p is weakly zero, denoted by $F \simeq 0$, if F vanishes when its variables are restricted to $\Gamma_p : F/\Gamma_p = 0$. By distinction F is strongly zero, $F \simeq 0$, if F and its first partial derivatives vanish when restricted to Γ. Thus

$$F = 0 \qquad F/\Gamma_p = 0 \qquad \text{(weak)}$$

$$F = 0 \qquad F/\Gamma_p = \partial F/\Gamma_p = 0 \qquad \text{(strong)}.$$

(ii) The division of the constraints into *first class* and *second class*. Thus the constraint φ is first class if its Poisson bracket $\{\varphi, \psi\}$ with any constraint ψ vanishes (where $\{\varphi, \psi\} = \partial \varphi/\partial q_r \cdot \partial \psi/\partial p_r - \partial \varphi/\partial p_r \cdot \partial \psi/\partial q_r$). Otherwise the constraint φ is termed second class.

These notions allowed Dirac to extend the idea of a Hamiltonian from the constrained Hamiltonian $H_c = \Sigma_r \, p_r \, \dot{q}_r - L$ by addition of a set of arbitrary coefficients μ_s multiplied by the set of constraints φ_s to give the unconstrained Hamiltonian

$$H = \sum p_r \, \dot{q}_r - L + \sum \mu_s \varphi_s. \qquad (5)$$

Then the equations of motion for any dynamical variable A now involve the notion of weak equality introduced above and have the expected Hamiltonian form

$$\dot{A} \simeq \{A, H_c\} + \sum \mu_s \{A, \varphi_s\}. \qquad (6)$$

The constraints must be conserved in time, so that when A in (6) is replaced by one of the φ_s further constraints may then arise, of form

$$\chi = 0. \qquad (7)$$

These are to be distinguished from the original or primary constraints $\varphi = 0$, and were called secondary constraints by Anderson and Bergmann. In the example of electromagnetism given above the conservation constraint $\dot{\pi}_{A_0} = 0$ leads to the secondary constraint $\partial_i \pi^i = 0$. Since $\pi^i = E^i$ (the electric field components), this just corresponds to Gauss's law. Requiring the conservation of the secondary constraints may lead to tertiary (and higher) constraints. This process of generating further constraints may be shown to stop after a finite number of steps, giving the final constrained phase space Γ_c; a summary of how this occurs is given concisely in Dirac (1964).[4] This process has also been described in an elegant geometrical fashion more recently.[7]

In general, conservation of the first-class constraints φ_J will give no conditions on the associated coefficients μ_J in (5). These μ_J are thus to be regarded as the same degrees of freedom as the $(N - R)$ arbitrary functions $\dot{q}_r$ mentioned earlier. On the other hand conservation of the second-class constraint φ will in general determine the corresponding μ_j. Using the values of these latter quantities Dirac then showed how the equations of motion (6) could be written in the suggestive form

$$\dot{A} \simeq \{A, H_c\}_{\text{DB}} \tag{8}$$

where the Dirac bracket is defined by

$$\{A, B\}_{\text{DB}} \equiv \{A, B\} - \{A, \varphi_j\} P_{jk}^{-1}\{\varphi_k, B\} \tag{9}$$

where $P_{jk} = \{\varphi_j, \varphi_k\}$ and the matrix P can be shown to be invertible.

We can understand this simplication (8) by choosing as local coordinates the variables $Q_j = f_j$, $P_k = g_k$, where we may equally divide the even number of primary constraints into equivalent constraints (f_j, g_k), which are canonical variables with $\{Q_i, Q_j\} = \{P_i, P_j\} = 0$, $\{Q_i, P_j\} = \delta_{ij}$. We may complete the variables Q, P by further variables X, Y in such a way that the Poisson bracket of a variable in terms of the new set (Q, P, X, Y) is the Dirac bracket in terms of the original variables. We thus obtain the notion of the *reduced phase space,* which may be regarded as that obtained by solving the second-class constraints in terms of ignoring the variables Q, P above and only keeping dependence on the reduced phase space variables X, Y.

It is in terms of these latter variables that physical questions about the constrained system should be discussed. However, whilst the above procedure is possible for second-class constraints in a wide range of situations, that is not the case for first-class ones, for which the same local reduction of phase space is still possible in principle. Thus it may be impossible to extend the above local procedure globally in such a way that Γ_c is the tangent space to a manifold. Moreover, in most cases of interest (Yang–Mills, gravity, strings) it is not possible to find an explicit form of the canonical variables for the reduced phase space.

Because of this crucial difficulty it is usual to handle first-class constraints (for which the matrix P in (9) vanishes identically) by introducing a further set of constraints, Ω_J, called the gauge fixing constraints, so that the matrix analogous to P, $\{\varphi_J, \Omega_K\}$, is invertible. For example, for electromagnetism we may take $\Omega_1 = A_0$, $\Omega_2 = \partial_i A_i$, for the so-called radiation gauge. We note, however, that gauge fixing is not always possible, since a particular set of Ω may not uniquely fix the gauge (Gribov's disease[9]). This is a problem for the Coulomb or Lorentz gauges for Yang–Mills theories.

Finally we note that, for theories with first-class constraints, a natural definition of an observable F is one which is weakly gauge invariant under transformations generated by the φ_J:

$$\{F, \varphi_J\}_{DB} \simeq 0. \tag{10}$$

Dirac also gave much thought to the quantisation of constrained systems. The approach he advocated[4] involved identifying the Dirac bracket for two dynamical quantities as the commutator bracket of the corresponding quantum mechanical operators (so handling the second-class constraints), and imposing the first-class constraints on the physical states of $|\text{phys}\rangle$ of the system

$$\varphi_J |\text{phys}\rangle = 0. \tag{11}$$

The treatment of first- and second-class constraints has more recently been developed in the path integral approach, for which there are various useful features. This has led to the Faddeev–Popov ghost fields and interactions[10] and the extension of this to covariant constraints.[11]

There are numerous directions in which the discipline of constrained dynamics is developing. This is indicated by the wide range of open problems currently being tackled. Amongst these are the following.

(i) Attempts to discover the canonical group, and so lead to a more general analysis of quantisation. This has been particularly developed by Isham and his students.[12] Mention can be given here to the recent analysis of anomalies and their description in terms of deformations of the Dirac bracket of (9) by Bakas and Kakas.[13]

(ii) Proof of the conjecture that the configuration space Q for Yang–Mills field theories, that is the quotient space Q = gauge connections/gauge transformations, is equal to the space of Wilson loops, or gauge invariant functionals $W(C)$ on loops C defined by

$$\left| W(C) = \left\langle 0 \left| T\left[\exp\left(i \int_i A \cdot du\right)\right] \right| 0 \right\rangle \right. .^{14}$$

(iii) Separation of first- and second-class constraints for the superparticle and for superstrings.[15] The difficulty here is that, for a massless superparticle described by the additional fermionic variable θ besides its position vector x, with action $\int du\,(\dot{x}^\mu - \bar{\theta}\gamma^\mu\dot{\theta})^2$ (where γ^μ are the Dirac matrices) the primary constraints are

$$\varphi_\alpha = p_\alpha - i(\not{p}\theta)_\alpha = 0$$

We have denoted by p_α the momentum associated with θ, and $\not{p} = p_\mu\gamma^\mu$. But since also $p^2 = 0$, the matrix $\{\varphi_\alpha, \varphi_\beta\} = (\not{p})_{\alpha\beta}$ is not invertible. This difficulty arises due to a mixing of first- and second-class constraints which is known to be resolvable by using a non-Lorentz covariant gauge (the light-cone gauge first introduced by Dirac in 1949[16]), but not in a covariant manner. The same problem arises for superstrings. The superparticle difficulty may be partly resolved by means of introducing an extra dimension to act as a central charge following Azcarraga and Lukierski,[17] though the quantisation of such a formalism meets the difficulties associated with problem (iv) below.[18] The problem for superstrings can be solved formally by the introduction of suitable gauge fixing constraints but then leads to q-number Dirac brackets and the associated difficulties of factor ordering.[19]

(iv) The construction of full superfield forms of maximally extended supersymmetric Yang–Mills and supergravity theories. This latter theory had been seriously proposed as a candidate for the ultimate theory of the universe. However, the proof of the finiteness or otherwise of S-matrix elements for that theory has so far eluded us, as also remarked on by Professor Salam in his talk. Attempts using central charges have made some progress,[18] but the situation is still unclear.

(v) Construction of a fully covariant theory of strings and superstrings, which incorporates the full gauge invariances of the massless states. Some progress has been made in this,[20] and in view of the expected finiteness of on-shell amplitudes for closed superstrings[21] this question is of great interest for further analysis of superstring theory. I have not given any details on the pioneering work done by Paul Dirac on the problem of quantising the gravitational field, though this is discussed in his elegant lectures[4] and in his fundamental paper.[22] The canonical analysis of gravity has developed considerably, but I felt that the subject was too technical to analyse usefully here and refer anyone interested to the above papers. For more recent work try the references in Isham's book.[12]

I hope I have by now persuaded you that constrained dynamics is a vigorous discipline which owes much of its present direction to Paul Dirac's clear-sighted vision as to what were the important concepts. As described in the second lesson at the moving Commemorative service held for Dirac in St John's Chapel 'if therefore thine eye be single, thy whole body shall be full of light'. Paul Dirac had, indeed, that singleness of vision which has given mathematical physics much illumination.

To conclude on a more personal note, but bearing out the last remark, I heard from Abraham Pais that the first time he met Paul Dirac was at the Institute for Advanced Study in Princeton. He (Pais) was just buying some milk in the refectory and Dirac said to him, as he came up to him 'Can you get milk here?' 'Yes' was the reply 'if you ask for it at the counter' (the milk was hidden away in a refrigerator to keep it fresh). Apparently Pais went and sat down, and did not speak to Dirac for the remainder of the academic year for which Dirac was visiting Princeton. Seven years later, Dirac's sabbatical year having come round again, he walked past Pais one lunchtime as the latter was seated in the refectory at the Institute. 'You are still drinking milk, I see' was Dirac's single-minded comment.

References

1   Dirac P A M 1950 *Can. J. Math.* **2** 129
2   Dirac P A M 1951 *Can. J. Math.* **3** 1
3   Dirac P A M 1958 *Proc. R. Soc.* A **246** 326
4   Dirac P A M 1964 *Lectures on Quantum Mechanics* (New York: Belfer Graduate School of Science, Yeshiva University)
5   Sundermeyer K 1982 *Constrained Dynamics* (Berlin: Springer)
6   Marmo G, Mukunda N and Samuel J 1983 *Riv. Nuovo Cim.* **6** 1
7   Anderson J L and Bergmann P G 1951 *Phys. Rev.* **83** 1018
8   Gotay M J, Nestor J M and Hinds G 1978 *J. Math. Phys.* **19** 2388
9   Gribov V N 1978 *Nucl. Phys.* B **139** 1
10 Faddeev L and Popov V N 1967 *Phys. Lett.* **25B** 29
11 Fradkin E S and Vilkovisky G A 1973 *Phys. Rev.* D **8** 4241
12 Isham C J 1984 in *Relativity, Groups and Topology II* (Amsterdam: North Holland)
13 Bakas I and Kakas A C 1985 Quantization and deformations and String anomalies through deformations, *Imperial College Preprints* (April 1985)
14 See, for instance, Neveu A 1984 in *Recent Advances in Field Theory and Statistical Mechanics* ed J-B Zuber and R Stora (Amsterdam: North Holland)
15 Green M B and Schwarz J H 1982 *Phys. Lett.* **109B** 444; Green M B and Schwarz J H 1984 *Phys. Lett.* **136B** 367 R2
16 Dirac P A M 1949 *Rev. Mod. Phys.* **21** 392
17 Azcarraga J de and Lukierski H 1982 *Phys. Lett.* **133B** 170
18 Taylor J G Maximal super Yang–Mills and supergravity in full superspace in *Proc. Int. Coll. Applications of Group Theory in Theor. Phys., Maryland Univ.* (to be published); Card C T, Davis P R, Restuccia A and Taylor J G *Phys. Lett.*
19 Hori T and Kamimura K 1985 Canonical formulation of superstring *University of Kyoto Preprint*
20 Neveu A and West P C in *Proc. Supersymmetry and Supergravity Workshop, Cambridge, 1985* ed G Gibbons, S Hawking and P Townsend (Cambridge: Cambridge University Press) (to be published)

21 Mandelstam S private communication; Restuccia A and Taylor J G in *Proc. Int. High Energy Phys. Conf., Bari, 1985* (to be published)

22 Dirac P A M 1958 *Proc. R. Soc.* A **246** 333